# Simon Peter
# and the
# Master

# Simon Peter and the Master

Rhonda Calhoun

HEART
PUBLISHING

**Simon Peter and the Master**
by Rhonda Calhoun

Other books by Rhonda Calhoun:
THE BRIDE
BLESSED ARE THE POOR
KID'S EXPLOSION MANUAL
THE BRIDE OF CHRIST STUDY MANUAL
THE FATHER HEART OF GOD STUDY MANUAL

Heart Publishing
12905 South 71 Hwy. #177
Grandview, MO  64030
harvesthome@juno.com
www.harvesthome.org
816-522-9011

Printed in the United States of America
International Standard Book Number: 0-9719140-2-8

Special thanks to:
Cover design by Dan Arnold
darnold@kc.rr.com

Edited by Edie Veach
ironsharp@flmtgif.org

*This book is dedicated to*
*my Beloved Savior,*
*for He has been so good to me!*

# TABLE OF CONTENTS

# FOREWORD

There is no topic in this earth greater or more life-changing than the glorious Man, Christ Jesus. He is a Lion and a Lamb, a King and a Shepherd, a Savior and a Judge, a Master and a Servant. He is the image of the invisible God, the firstborn of all creation. All things were created by Him and for Him. He is before all things, and in Him all things hold together. He is the head of the church, and He is the beginning—the firstborn from the dead—in order that He might come to have first place in everything (Colossians 1:15-18). There is absolutely nothing as important or as wonderful as knowing the King of kings! This was Simon Peter's passion—to know Him even in the fellowship of His sufferings!

It is for this very reason that I highly recommend Rhonda's newest book, Simon Peter and the Master. This book unveils the nature and character of God in a way that ignites the heart and strengthens the spirit. You will be challenged by the love and devotion seen in the life of Peter and demonstrated during his imprisonment for the cause of his Master.

Rhonda portrays the relationship of Simon Peter and

the Master through Peter's perspective. We have no gospel according to Peter, but Rhonda skillfully presents Peter's account by using the events portrayed in the four gospels. In a concise way she reveals the beauty of God's grace, the endless nature of His unconditional love, the depths of His unfailing mercy, the power of His extravagant forgiveness, and the tremendous mark all of these left on Simon Peter. This book clearly draws out of the human heart a deep desire to be transformed into the image of the beautiful Man Christ Jesus, to worship Him, to spend time with Him, and to live a life of utter abandonment for the sake of the King. Experiencing these realities can change your life.

I have worked with Rhonda since 1995, witnessing her genuine life of devotion and sacrificial service to the poor and the outcast. She is a remarkable testimony of the grace of God joining together the extravagant devotion of Mary of Bethany with the servant heart of her sister, Martha. I am truly grateful for the inspiration to godliness that Rhonda's life imparts to the staff at the International House of Prayer.

I am confident that your heart and life will be impacted by *Simon Peter and the Master.* This book is filled with truth and mercy and love—a love that never fails to overwhelmingly effect and change those who receive it, even those in Nero's dungeon.

Mike Bickle
Director,
International House of Prayer of Kansas City

# AUTHOR'S NOTE

If Peter had written a gospel account of his relationship with Jesus Christ, what would he have said? If we could have seen Peter later in his life—during his final imprisonment—what would we find him doing?

*Simon Peter and the Master* is my attempt to provide answers to these questions. After compiling events from the four gospels and applying the words of Peter from His epistles, I have written *Simon Peter and the Master* in an attempt to reveal God's infinite heart for His children as experienced through Peter's eyes.

I have presented the gospel events in the order of their occurrence rather than the order they are related in the New Testament, which gives a greater understanding of the day-to-day interaction Jesus had with both His disciples and the people of the land. In the few instances where it is not quite clear when or where a particular event happened, I placed the event in the story when or where it seemed to most likely have occurred.

I have diligently sought to portray each event in the same manner it is related in the Scriptures. In some instances, I included additional dialogues to help further explain the subject being discussed. I have also included various commentaries and references concerning the Jewish customs of the day, which further helps bring the Scriptures to light.

What a delight it was to write this book! My prayer is that you would be transformed by the Master's great love as you explore the delightful mysteries awaiting you. And, first and foremost, I pray that Jesus Christ would be glorified through this book, for He is the reason we live!

In the beginning was the Word,
and the Word was with God,
and the Word was God.

He was in the beginning with God.

All things came into being by Him,
and apart from Him nothing came into being
that has come into being.

In Him was life,
and the life was the Light of men.
The Light shines in the darkness,
and the darkness did not comprehend it.

And the Word became flesh,
and dwelt among us, and we saw His glory,
glory as of the only begotten from the Father,
full of grace and truth.

John 1:1-5, 14

# CHAPTER ONE

It is the year 67 A.D. and I, Simon Peter, son of John, am a prisoner of Jesus Christ. Nero, emperor of Rome, ordered me put in solitary confinement after condemning me to death for being a follower of the one true God. This is certainly not how I would have written the pages of my life, but I trust the One who knows the end from the beginning and always has my best interest at heart.

As for the month, day, or hour, I cannot say for certain. There are no windows in this dungeon, so I have been unable to determine the end of one day from the beginning of another.

I sit in thick, absolute darkness; my hands and feet chained to a rough, wooden post. I have been in solitary confinement since my arrest.

The not so distant sound of clanging keys and shuffling of feet warns me that I am probably about to undergo my routine torture. "Father, grant me the grace to endure whatever may come my way," I quickly pray.

The prison door opens, and a guard shouts, "Stop your praying, Christian!"

A torch is shoved in my face, the flames singe my beard and skin. The sickening smell of burning hair fills my nostrils causing my empty stomach to churn.

I silently ask the Lord for the grace to love this man and then say, "Brutus, my friend, have you decided to heed the good news that I have spoken to you nearly every day now for who knows how long?"

Brutus angrily shouts, "I am indeed ready to respond, Christian! I am ready to demonstrate how foolish you are, how stupid you are!"

He places his torch in the holder just outside the door and quickly returns to my side. "Here is what I think of your good news."

He grabs my hair yanking my head back; it feels as though he will surely break my neck.

"If your God is truly all that you claim him to be then let him come and rescue you from the likes of me," Brutus mocks.

With agonizing precision, Brutus rips out chunks of my beard leaving gaping holes in my face. I think back to another time and place, to an hour when my beloved Master had His beard plucked. I remind myself that my afflictions are light in comparison to all that Jesus endured. I am very aware that my suffering is temporary and that it is producing in me an eternal weight of glory far beyond anything I could ever imagine.

One day it will be worth it all, I tell myself.

Even this senseless torture is being used by the Lord to make me more like Him. This comforts me greatly, for more than anything, I long to be like my beloved Master and King. Many years ago, I made a decision that I would live my life as Jesus lived His. Therefore, I have set my face like flint on the beauty and wonders of Jesus, for He sustains me. I continually remind myself of the glory that awaits me when I take my last breath.

Brutus continues to taunt me, yet I remain silent. I will not join in his ungodly ways; I will not fight back; I will not hate. I will love even my enemies, for this is how the Master lived His life and how He instructed us to live. I whisper, "Father, forgive Brutus because he does not know what he is doing."

Brutus trembles with rage as he glares down at me. "I don't know what I am doing, you say! I know exactly what I am doing! I am plucking out the beard of a stupid Jew who dares to believe in the tales of old women and ignorant men!"

After slamming my face into the post, he storms out. Blood gushes from my nose; it feels broken, again.

The torch remains, and the door stands open, a sure sign that Brutus plans to return. Unfortunately, I am right. Only moments later, Brutus returns accompanied by three other guards. Not knowing what evil scheme he has planned, I silently cry out for heaven's intervention and protection.

Grabbing my hair, Brutus again forces my head back. My face throbs; I choke on the blood running down my throat. I look up just before Brutus empties the contents of a bucket over my head. Human excrement covers my face and body. The smell is more than I can tolerate, and my stomach convulses.

Brutus continues to hold my head back as I struggle to breathe. Fearing that he will either break my neck or I will choke to death, I desperately and silently cry out for God to intervene.

Sudden shouts from the hallway cause Brutus to release his hold on me. To my relief, a fierce disagreement has erupted among several of the guards. Throwing my head forward, Brutus angrily says, "I *will* be back."

Blood mixed with vomit spews out of my mouth and nose. "Oh, dear Master, I remember. I remember the price You paid, the suffering You endured. I remember how You shed Your blood for me, and it is enough; it is enough for me."

Once order is restored, Brutus returns only to slip on my vomit. Cursing, he grabs the post to keep from falling. A guard is summoned, and Brutus shouts, "It seems we have a mess in here. Bring me the other bucket!"

My nose and face are throbbing so violently that I am dizzy. The guard returns with a bucket in hand. "Come in here," Brutus shouts to the other guards, "I am sure you will enjoy the show."

With my eyes tightly closed, I brace myself and pray. Before the contents reach my face, I can smell the strong, pungent odor of vinegar. My body shakes violently as the acidic liquid pours over my raw and bleeding face. It is difficult to breathe; waves of nausea and dizziness nearly overcome me. I force myself to silently worship, *"To*

*You, O Lord, I lift up my soul. O my God, in You I trust. Do not let me be ashamed; do not let my enemies exult over me. Remember, O Lord, Your compassion and Your lovingkindness, for they have been from of old. Do not remember the sins of my youth or my transgressions. According to Your lovingkindness remember me, for Your goodness' sake, Oh Lord."[1]*

"So, tell me, are you now ready to deny this Jesus? Have you had enough?" Brutus asks laughing.

"By the grace of God, I shall never again deny my Lord," I respond.

"Then I shall never stop making your life miserable," he answers.

With his face pressed close to mine he says, "I *will* break you! Before it is over, I will add you to my long list of weak Christians who came to their senses and denied this *Jesus*." Spittle showers my face.

With a mocking, evil laugh Brutus departs followed closely by the other guards.

I cannot wipe my face or eyes. I am totally helpless except for this one thing that no one can take away from me and that is my ability to commune with my God and King.

*Oh, divine Master, send help, I pray! Turn to me and be gracious to me, for I am lonely and afflicted. The troubles of my heart are great; bring me out of my distresses. You are my refuge and my portion in the land of the living. Give heed to my cry, for I am brought very low; deliver me from my persecutors, for they are too strong for me. Bring my soul out of prison, so that I may give thanks to Thy name! I love You and worship you, for You alone are worthy! Great is the Lord and greatly to be praised![2]*

A key turning in the lock causes me to cringe. Like an animal caught in a trap, my heart races. I frantically and silently cry out for help.

*I do not know how much more I can take, O Lord!*

Great relief floods over me as I hear the familiar voice of my good friend and fellow believer.

"Have no fear, it is I, Tiberias."

*I praise you Lord for sending Tiberias!*

I dare not respond for fear that more contamination will get into my mouth. Carefully and ever so gently, Tiberias quickly sets about the task of removing the gross matter from my face and neck. "Peter, my brother, I heard what they did to you and came as soon as it was safe, but I must hurry lest I am caught. I could not bear the thought of you being left in such a despicable state."

I merely grunt in response. Tiberias continues, "Peter, I am afraid I have bad news for you. Tomorrow they are moving you to a holding cell, for your execution is nigh."

He continues to work in silence and I think back to that dark day when I denied Jesus, not just once, but three times.

*Oh, Lord do not ever let me deny You again, I pray!*

Once all the excrement has been removed, I look into the kind eyes of my friend. The dim light from his torch reveals his deep concern for me. I comfort him with these words, "On the day of my departure from this world, do not mourn, my friend, for I will be with our beloved Master and King!"

Tiberias gently covers my face with oil of myrrh, being extra careful of the strips of skin hanging from my chin and cheeks. "I'm afraid your nose is most likely broken, but at least the bleeding has stopped," he says, his voice filled with compassion.

Because my hands are in chains, he holds a flask to my mouth for which I am extremely grateful. I rinse my mouth several times before I dare swallow. Tiberias breaks off a piece of bread and places it in my mouth. It is painful to chew, but my hunger exceeds my discomfort. He feeds me until I can eat no more. "I believe that was the best bread I have ever tasted," I say.

"I will be sure and tell my wife. She prayed that I would have an opportunity to give it to you. I only regret that it is under such painful circumstances."

"Please tell Lydia that her bread has brought strength to my body and encouraged my soul."

He gives me another drink of the wonderful water while praying for my healing. I think back to the day when the Master stood before a crowd and made the startling announcement that He was the living water. He invited everyone who was thirsty to come and drink that they might never thirst again. Oh, how I miss the Master's comforting presence! Oh, how I long to sit with Him and look into His kind eyes, eyes that saw the very act of creation!

Tiberias whispers, "Peter, I will come again as soon as I can. Stay true, my brother, for the Lord is with you."

"Thank you for your kindness to this old man. Your deeds have not gone unnoticed. Now go before you are discovered," I say, ever so grateful for his willingness to risk his life to comfort and assist me.

"Peter, may I be so bold as to remind you what you said to me on the day I accepted Jesus as my Lord and Savior?"

"Of course. You may speak anything that is on your heart, my friend."

"You told me that knowing Jesus was worth whatever price I had to pay, whatever suffering might come my way! Peter, after nine months in this torture chamber, do you still believe that? Peter, it is still true, is it not?"

*Has it truly been nine months?*

"Oh, my friend, Jesus is indeed worth it all!"

"In my heart of hearts I know it is true, but there are times when I wonder, times like this when you are so violently mistreated," Tiberias replies as he quickly gathers his things.

"Perfect love casts out all fear, my friend.[3] Always, in every circumstance, keep your focus on the Lord."

"I will remember your words, Peter," he responds as he turns to go.

"It will indeed be worth it all," I whisper to myself.

My nose throbs, and my face feels as though it is on fire, but I feel the nearness of my beloved Lord, which never fails to bring me great comfort.

*Is that His voice I hear? It sounds like a distant waterfall, powerful yet, at the same time, gentle and comforting.*

I strain to hear. His words become crystal clear, *"Peter, I am with you. I will never leave you nor forsake you!"*

I close my eyes and fall into His wonderful arms where I quickly fall asleep only to be wakened by a heavy boot kicking my backside. A voice that I do not recognize shouts, "Simon, son of John, also known as Peter, Nero, emperor of Rome, has ordered your execution. You are being moved to the holding cell where you will be led to your execution in a matter of days."

He laughs, obviously enjoying my plight. Unlocking my chains, he commands me to stand and follow him. What he has ordered me to do is absolutely impossible. I have been starved; I am nothing but skin and bones. I have sat in a bent, stooped position for so long that it is impossible for me to stand upright.

In my weakness, I respond, "I would like to obey, but my body is physically unable to comply."

My inability to stand only angers him further. Grabbing the chains attached to my wrists, he drags me out of my cell and down the corridor. The rough stones rip the flesh on my stomach, legs and feet. I struggle to remain conscious.

I remind myself of the words I have said to many believers through the years: *If anyone suffers as a Christian, let him not feel ashamed, but in that name let him glorify God. Therefore, let those also who suffer according to the will of God entrust their souls to a faithful Creator in doing what is right.*

*Lord, I choose to glorify You in the midst of my suffering and I entrust my very life to You.*[4]

I am dragged up a flight of stairs, around a corner, then up another flight. My arms feel as though they are being pulled out of their sockets.

*Oh, Lord—Your joints were pulled out of socket as You hung on that cruel cross. Your body was battered; Your flesh hung in strips. This is nothing, Lord, in comparison to what You suffered. Lord, I endure this for You; this is for love!*

I am suddenly and abruptly dropped to the floor. The guard mutters to himself as he unlocks a door. My stomach churns as warm blood once again gushes out of my nose and down my throat.

Grabbing my chains the guard drags me into a dark room saying,

"If your God is so good, why doesn't He help you now?"

"You have no power over me except what God allows. Suffering is not always a bad thing," I answer.

Cursing, the guard chains my ankles and wrists to a post then leaves without saying a word. I vomit just before passing out. Only God knows how long I am unconscious.

I fight my way through the thick fog that has settled over my mind and dulled my senses. I hear the sound of snoring, which lets me know that I am no longer in solitary confinement. Lifting my aching head, I desperately try to focus on my surroundings but find it impossible as the pain once more overwhelms me and I pass out.

I wake sometime later with a much clearer mind. The stench in this place is nauseating, and the heat is suffocating, but my heart soars. "Why?" you may ask. My heart soars because I am loved by the Master and the day is drawing near when I will be reunited with the great King. On that day, I will look back and declare that He was worth every beating, every scourging, every torment and every torture. On that day, Jesus Himself will wipe away every tear from my eyes, and I will fall at His feet and cast my crown before Him. Oh, what a glorious day that will be!

Feeling quite encouraged, I set about the task of getting to know my fellow prisoners only to discover that they are not in the least interested in getting to know me, much less being my friend.

The darkness in this place equals what I would imagine hell to be like. I am not sure just how many companions I now have; from the various noises I would guess there are four or five of us, but I am not certain. This may sound strange, but I find myself overjoyed at the thought that I now have company, even if that company is completely unsocial.

Time passes slowly. My broken nose is healing, but my face feels as though it is infected. I am unable to do anything about it because of my chains.

Images of the Master hanging on the cross fill my mind. I can hear John's voice even now saying, "Peter, I have never seen a sight more beautiful and, at the same time, more terrible than the sight of the

Master nailed to that piece of wood, battered beyond belief, beyond recognition."

Remembering keeps me from getting into self-pity and reminds me that I have nothing to complain about.

A bug crawls across my face. Carefully rubbing my face against the post, I manage to rid myself of the pest. Resting my cheek against the rough wood, I ask for the grace needed to finish my race. I long to finish with love in my heart. It would be easy to become angry and bitter, but I refuse to allow anything that is contrary to the nature and character of Jesus to become part of my life. I refuse to dwell on the injustices done to me. I have learned that persecution, pain and suffering will bring with them either growth or bitterness. My response determines whether I walk in victory or defeat, misery or peace. Every day I choose to love; I choose to forgive; I choose life.

In the thirty-four years since the Master's death, I have learned the importance of worship in the midst of persecution. My songs are often heard by passing guards who let me know in various painful ways that they do not appreciate my joyful spirit. But how can a soul not worship One who is so glorious? How can a soul not adore the One who gives us the gift of eternal life, a gift that can never be earned neither is it deserved? This gift of infinite love and complete forgiveness is more precious to me than anything this world has to offer. Therefore, my soul must sing; my soul must worship!

Because of my chains, I am forced to sit hunched over, which is extremely painful. I try desperately to find some relief for my aching back. Nearby, I hear a rodent frantically searching for food; it will find none since we have had neither bread nor water in what I would guess to be several days now. My mouth and throat are parched, but my soul is immersed in Living Water because of the One who loves me and died in my place. I know that the time of my departure from this earth draws near, and I will soon be reunited with my Savior. That knowledge fills me with great peace and joyful anticipation.

I think back over the many months that I have spent in complete darkness, enduring monstrous tortures, manacled to a post, sitting in my own waste, unable to lay down and so alone. It has been extremely difficult and quite painful, but it has been so worth it because Malchus, Tiberias, Processus, and forty-seven other guards have come to know Jesus as the Christ, the Messiah, the Son of God! All that I have gone through, all that I have endured has been worth it, for who can put a price on a soul? I certainly cannot. God alone determines human worth, and He clearly demonstrated His idea of our worth on Calvary's hill in the fact that He sacrificed His dearly loved Son that we might be forgiven and live with our heavenly Father for all eternity. Oh, what love, what matchless love my Savior gave to me!

The shackles around my wrists and ankles have made deep gouges in my skin. Suffering has indeed been a good friend to me, for I, like my Lord, have learned obedience through the things I have suffered. Suffering has a way of chiseling away those things within that are less than beneficial and are contrary to the nature and character of a follower of Christ. I have learned to embrace suffering rather than run from it.

The time of my departure from this life is nearly here. I have fought the good fight; I have finished the course, I have kept the faith. One day soon I will be standing before my King in eternity! What joy floods my soul! I am perfectly content; I am satisfied. I am more than ready to be reunited with my Master and Savior, my beloved Bridegroom King!

I think back to the day of my arrest. Nero, the ruler of Rome, publicly proclaimed himself to be the chief enemy of God. He then ordered the arrest and slaughter of all who follow Jesus. I was warned by fellow Christians to flee from Rome, which, at the time, seemed like the wise thing to do.

Later that night, my beloved wife and I were among a group of Christians secretly making our way out of Rome. We had just stepped outside the city gate when the Spirit of God spoke to me instructing me to stay in Rome.

Loving the Lord more than my life, I bid my friends farewell explaining that I must obey the Lord whatever the cost may be. My precious wife, Miriam, chose to remain with me knowing that it certainly and most probably would result in our arrest and quite possibly our death. The following day, after a woman was cleansed from leprosy, we were arrested and brought before Nero who condemned us to die because we refused to deny the Lord.

I have not seen Miriam since that day. I do not know if she is alive or if she has departed this earth for a better place. I miss her greatly. She has been such an encouragement to me and so many others throughout our many years together. Not once has she ever complained about the hardships we have endured, neither has she hesitated to follow the Lord where ever He should lead. Our life together has been filled with great sacrifice and hardship but also tremendous joy and delight.

My cell mates are silent, which can only mean that they are asleep, so I quietly worship:

> "I will always love You, Lord.
> I will always sing to You!
> I will always put you first
> because there is no one like You!
> You are outstanding among ten thousand,
> more glorious than the sun and
> more beautiful than the sons of men!"

Suddenly, out of the darkness, a voice says, "My name is Justus, and I must know—how can you sing when you are about to die?"

"Justus, it is so good to make your acquaintance. My name is Simon Peter. You can call me Peter, for that is what the Master called me.

"To answer your question, I rejoice because I am infinitely loved by Jesus of Nazareth. He has redeemed me from the pit of hell, forgiven my sins and placed a crown of life on my head. A day is soon coming when I will stand before Him, and on that day, I will be more alive than I have ever been. On that day, He will welcome me into His eternal home, and I will never be separated from Him again. I will never again struggle with sin neither will I suffer any pain or sorrow. I will lay my crown at His feet because He alone is deserving of any honor or praise. In that moment, my joy will be complete.

"Justus, this world holds no attraction for me. There is a glorious place waiting for all those who give themselves to Jesus, surrendering their all to Him. There is nothing that I desire more than to spend eternity with my Lord and King."

Justus responds, "I am a murderer and a thief; there is no hope for me. But you can save yourself by simply denying that you are a Christian."

"There is hope for everyone, my friend, even murderers and thieves. As for me, what you propose is more painful to me than the torture I endure daily. You see, my friend, I fear God more than I fear man. The deepest disgrace and the most painful event in life would be for me to deny the Master—I would rather die than to turn my back on Him!"

My words are met with a long silence. I begin to wonder if he has fallen asleep. Justus finally responds, "Will you tell me about Him? Will you tell me about this Jesus?"

"There is nothing I would rather do, my friend." I say as I lean my cheek against the post. "My story begins on a bright autumn morning in the year 30 A.D. My brother, Andrew, and I had been fishing on the Sea of Galilee. I was tired and, I must admit, a bit irritable since we had fished all night and caught absolutely nothing.

"I was a young man then, only twenty-one years of age."

## CHAPTER TWO

Jumping out of the boat, Andrew and I dragged our nets to the shore. Our fishing partners, James and John and their father, Zebedee, were busy mending their nets a short distance away. Having secured our boat, Andrew and I began the arduous task of washing the sand and pebbles from our nets.[5] After a long night on the sea, having caught nothing, I was thoroughly exhausted and eager to return home to my lovely wife and the wonderful breakfast that she would surely have waiting for me.

As we worked, the bright, morning sun burned away the thick fog that hovered over the water during the night. It promised to be another glorious day, but one that I would not see a lot of because I desired only two things—a hearty breakfast and a good, long sleep.

I finished washing the first net then picked up a second when I heard a familiar voice, a voice that never failed to capture my attention. A large crowd had gathered on the beach, making it impossible to locate the speaker. Jumping on the foremost part of my boat, I discovered, just as I suspected, that the One who had drawn so many people to this remote place was Jesus of Nazareth. He had only recently become quite popular in Capernaum.

Being Jewish, I had grown up sitting at the feet of rabbis, but their teaching did not compare with the fire that burned deep within this Rabbi. His messages were unlike anything I had ever heard. He taught as one having great authority, yet His messages were filled with unconditional love. But, do not misunderstand me. Even though His messages were filled with love, they were also precise and to the point—cutting through the rabbinical traditions as easily as a knife cuts through butter.

Perched on the bow of my boat, I thought back to the first time I heard of this Man. It was January, a day just like any other day. I had gone to the wilderness to hear a prophet named John the baptizer.

John was an odd sort of fellow. He lived between the center of Judea and the Dead Sea. The home he chose for himself was nothing more than a limestone desert where the rock was blistering hot; it seemed as though a fire burned beneath the ground.

When I asked John why he chose to live in this desolate place, he answered, "Solitude and suffering are good companions, Simon, for they have a way of driving mankind into the very heart of God."

At the time, I did not understand his words, but as the years passed, I soon experienced what he was talking about and came to understand.

John's way of life intrigued me. His diet consisted of locusts and wild honey. His clothing was nothing more than a rough garment made of camel's hair and a leather belt around his waist. It did not go unnoticed that he dressed in the same manner as the prophet Elijah, but more than his appearance reminded us of the prophets of old. Like them, John lived a simple life. He avoided the comforts and luxuries this world offered because he understood that they had the potential for killing the soul.[6]

It was not only John's appearance, or his strange diet or his simple life-style that fascinated me, but it was his powerful preaching that drew me like honey draws bees.

My people, the Jews, had waited for over three-hundred years to hear the voice of God through the prophets, for God had been painfully silent until John arrived. In John's voice, I heard truth and righteousness. Many of my people rejoiced that God had once again turned His face toward His chosen people.

John's fiery messages pointed to Something and to Someone beyond himself. His words brought such strong conviction that most who heard him cried out for help. He spoke of repentance, which he defined as not only turning away from your sins, but also hating the sin itself. He announced that his baptism immersed people in water, but there was One who would immerse us in the Holy Spirit. He taught that water merely cleansed the body, but there was One who would cleanse our soul, our lives, our hearts.

This was a brand new concept to us. As Jewish people, we believed that we would be saved simply because of our nationality. In our eyes, only the pagan nations needed to repent and convert to Judaism. Never had we, until John, even considered the idea that *we* needed to repent.

I was amazed at John's confidence when confronted by the Pharisees and the Scribes. He was able to boldly proclaim the truth because he was unafraid, which was a rare thing when dealing with these powerful men.

My brother, Andrew soon became one of John's closest and most loyal disciples.

There was a fire burning in John that kept me coming back to hear more. On one of those occasions, John, standing on a large rock, turned to the crowd and said, "There is One who is coming that is so great that I am not worthy to untie the thong of His sandals."[7]

*What is John talking about? Our roads are stony paths layered in dirt. In the dry months, they are dust bowls. In wet weather, they are rivers of mud mixed with animal waste. Because of this, only the lowest of servants are given the task of washing traveler's feet. The One John speaks of must be extremely important for John to say that he is not worthy of such a menial and degrading task.*

John announced that he was sent to prepare the way for this One who was the Messiah. He likened the Messiah to a Bridegroom and himself as simply the Bridegroom's friend. He repeatedly told us that when this One came we were to follow Him. John's teachings created in us a keen desire and deep longing to find the One he spoke of so often and so affectionately.

And so it was, on that January day, my brother, Andrew saw Him, the One John spoke of. Andrew sat on the bank of the Jordan river enjoying a bit of a rest while watching John baptize a long line of men and women in the murky waters. It was a day like a thousand others until John suddenly stopped. He looked up staring at something behind Andrew. His expression was one of delight and, at the same time, he appeared to be frightened.

Curious, Andrew looked over his shoulder. He saw nothing of any consequence, only a very common looking Man who was making His way towards the water's edge.

John remained transfixed.

The stranger was smiling broadly. There was an air of quiet dignity about Him yet deep humility.

John suddenly shouted, "Behold, the Lamb of God who takes away the sin of the world!"[8]

His words had not yet penetrated my brother's mind, much less his heart when John added, "This is the One I told you about! He is the reason I came baptizing people in water! I came that I might show Him to the people of Israel!"

Andrew's heart lept in his throat.

This Man appeared quite common. His garments were those of a simple laborer not those of a King. He looked just like any other man. He certainly did not look like the Lamb of God, whatever that might be.

The Stranger made His way to the water's edge and removed His outer garment, laid it across a large rock, then stepped into the muddy waters.

And all the while, John watched, unmoving and speechless. Eager to be close enough to see and hear what was about to transpire, Andrew quickly waded out.

The stranger stopped directly in front of John and said, "I have come to be baptized."

John responded, "I have need to be baptized by you, my Lord. Do you, the Son of God, come to me to be baptized?"

The Man laid His hand on John's shoulder and replied, "John, permit this, for I must fulfill all righteousness."[9]

From John's expression it was obvious that he was not sure what to do. The Man gently squeezed John's shoulder and smiled. John nodded in response. With trembling hands, John baptized the Stranger. Andrew watched as the Stranger was swallowed up in the clutches of a watery grave and then exploded out of the dark waters, free from its hold! Immediately, the Stranger was filled with great joy and lifted His voice in prayer.

Andrew realized that something powerful—something greater than anything the world had ever seen—had happened, but it would be quite some time before he understood exactly what it was.

John was also profoundly impacted as were the others standing in the water and on the shore. They, too, were captivated; the air was filled with anticipation.

The clouds suddenly parted like the Red Sea. The sun shone through, and in bodily form like that of a dove, the Holy Spirit descended on the Stranger's shoulder, remaining on Him. John quickly scrambled backwards nearly falling over. A voice like that of thunder spoke from heaven saying, "This is My beloved Son, in whom I am well pleased! Beloved as a Son is to His Father are You to Me!"[10]

Terrified, Andrew ran out of the water and scrambled on all fours up the beach, shaking like a leaf blowing in the wind.

He looked over his shoulder. The Man who caused the heavens to speak made His way out of the water. He was within an arm's length of Andrew when He stopped. For a brief moment, He looked deep into Andrew's eyes then smiled as if He knew him. With a nod, He picked up His garment then continued on. A speechless Andrew watched as the Stranger disappeared into the wilderness.

Andrew ran from there directly to me. He looked like a man who had seen a ghost. He related the events to me explaining that something had happened within him that he did not understand. He said that he felt like he had just met the gentlest, and at the same time, the most intense Man alive.

Forty days later, the day before the Sabbath, Andrew went to the wilderness to hear John preach as he often did. The next evening, I relaxed by the seashore, enjoying the solitude when Andrew came running toward me like a horse escaping from its pen.

Andrew stopped abruptly, and sand flew all over me. "What's got you so excited, little brother?" I asked.

Without taking time to catch his breath, he grabbed me by the shoulders and exclaimed, "I found Him! I've found the Messiah, the King of Israel!"

Pulling on my arm, he continued, "You must come and see, for I have spent the day with Him and I tell you that He is the one John told us would come!"

Amused and quite curious, I jumped up. "Then lead on, little brother."

It was all I could do to keep up with Andrew as he led me through the countryside. Finally, Andrew suddenly stopped. In the distance, several young men sat in a circle around a campfire. Andrew pointed to One among them and said, "There He is; He is the man John baptized on whom the Spirit, in a form like a dove, had rested and to whom the heavens spoke. He is the One John said was the Messiah, the King of Israel."

"*He* is the Messiah, the King of Israel?" I quietly asked perplexed by His rather unimpressive appearance.

"Simon, I am telling you that He is the One!"

"I agree that there might be something different about Him, but Andrew—the King of Israel, the Messiah? This is a serious statement that you make." I responded.

Andrew replied, "Simon, early this morning John, the son of Zebedee, and I were standing with John the baptizer when this man, whose name is Jesus, passed by. He stopped only long enough to acknowledge our presence then moved on without saying a word. But, Simon, He didn't need to say anything; His eyes said volumes. John the baptizer nearly scared me to death when he pointed after Him and shouted, 'Behold, the Lamb of God!'

"At that point, I was overcome by an irresistible desire to follow Him. Without even bidding the baptizer farewell, John and I ran after this One the baptizer called the Lamb of God. We had gone only a short distance when Jesus stopped and asked us, 'What do you seek?' We answered, 'Rabbi, where are You staying?' 'Come and you will see,' the Teacher replied.[11]

"Simon, we have sat at His feet all day listening to His words, which are full of life and hope and are wiser than any I have ever heard from any rabbi in Israel. Brother, come and hear Him for yourself so you will know that what I say is true."

*Could this common looking man truly be the King that all Israel has been looking for? The King who will deliver us from the oppressive rule of Rome?*

"Come!" Andrew said once more as he tugged on my sleeve.

Extremely curious, yet highly skeptical, I followed Andrew into the clearing. The Teacher waited until I was standing directly in front of Him before He acknowledged my presence. A knowing smile lit up His face as He warmly welcomed me.

I looked around the small group. The only ones I recognized were our fishing partners, John and his brother James, but as for the identity of the others, I was ignorant.

My gaze returned to the Rabbi whose features were rugged, yet He was cloaked in a gentleness that drew me. His face was quite tan and weather-worn; He had obviously spent much time outdoors. His hands were those of a manual laborer, and yet there was a gracefulness to them that was not common for one who works with his hands.

He looked at me with piercing eyes that penetrated my very being. I shuddered. Standing, He greeted me saying, "You are Simon, the son of John. You shall be called Peter."

*How does He know my name and the name of my father? Perhaps Andrew told Him. But why would He call me 'Peter'? Peter means 'rock'. What? Who is this Man that looks into the depths of my soul and calls me a rock?*

Stunned, I backed away. Andrew motioned for me to come and sit by his side.

The Rabbi resumed His teaching. His words were like living water to my soul. I drank deeply and found myself lost in the wonder of His message. My soul felt as though it was soaring like an eagle riding on the wind.

Unaware of anything but the sound of His voice, I listened intently until Andrew nudged me in the side whispering, "It is time for us to go."

Seeing us getting ready to depart, James and John stood to leave. Jesus bid the four of us farewell. With a nod, I followed Andrew. Once we were far enough away that I was certain the Teacher could not hear, I asked, "Andrew, did you tell Him my name?"

"No, brother, I did not. Neither did I tell Him our father's name."

"Then how did He know?"

Andrew shrugged in response.

"He called me a rock, Andrew! Did you hear Him? Did you hear Him call me that?"

"Of course, I did; I hung on His every word. It does not surprise me that He would call you that, brother. I have always known you to be like a rock! You are solid, resolute, dependable and strong in your convictions. And you always were a bit hardheaded," he responded as he playfully kicked my backside then took off.

I quickly overtook him, running all the way to the sea.

When Andrew, James and John finally arrived, I teased, "So what took you so long? I thought I was going to have to fish without you."

"Not everyone was born with wings, Simon," Andrew answered.

Within a short time, we were out to sea. Even though the night was long, my thoughts were on the Rabbi.

*Just what is it about this Man that fascinates me so? And how did He know my name and the name of my father? And why did He call me Peter? He knows nothing about me.*

The sun was rising, so we turned our boats toward home; the wind was contrary. Fighting with the sails, I realized that, even though I had more questions than answers concerning this Man, I was still excited. Why? I did not know, but my heart was filled with incredible peace and great joy, which was something I had not felt in a very long time.

# CHAPTER THREE

My story is interrupted by a rodent that has decided to make my foot its next meal. Unable to move more than a few inches, I frantically try to rid myself of the pest, but find it quite impossible.

"Peter, why did you stop? Tell me how He knew your name and the name of your father?" Justus pleads.

"I am encountering a hungry rat at the moment, my friend," I answer while furiously kicking my foot, "I will surely answer your questions once I have gotten rid of my unwelcome guest."

Having done everything within my power to chase it away only to have it continue nibbling on my toes, I cry out, "In the name of Jesus and by His authority I command you to leave me and this cell!"

With a loud screech, the rat quickly scampers away.

"What just happened?" Justus asks.

"I got rid of the rat."

"But, how?" he asks.

"God has given us authority on earth, authority over our enemies. And I have simply used that authority," I answer.[12]

"I've never heard of anything like that!" he responds.

"Jesus gives His followers great authority. Jesus was indeed the Messiah, but it took me quite some time to discover that truth. In the beginning, I thought Him to be simply a great Teacher, but I soon realized that He was much more than that. Then, I thought Him to be a Prophet, but I soon saw that He was even more than that. It was not until I had walked with the Master many months that I came to understand that He was indeed the Messiah, the Son of the living God who was sent to save mankind from their sins.[13]

"As for how He knew my name, there is nothing hidden from Jesus. He knows the end from the beginning and every detail in between. He even knows the secrets of my heart and yours."

"It is obvious that you became one of His followers," a new voice speaks from out of the deep darkness.

"It is with great joy that I confess that I am. And your name is?"

"I am Laban, the son of Ichthus."

"Laban, my friend, I am glad to make your acquaintance. To answer your question, I am a follower of Jesus, but it did not happen right away. As I spent time with Him and witnessed the miracles and experienced a kindness unlike anything I had ever seen, I became one of His followers, but even then I did not fully understanding who He was.

"Jesus was a man who walked in great compassion and lived a life of self-sacrifice. He restored sight to the blind, caused the lame to walk and embraced those who were outcasts. There was no one outside of His reach. He always pursued those lost in sin.

"After His death and resurrection, I came to fully understand that Jesus was God in a human body revealing to the world His glorious character and merciful nature. Lest I get ahead of myself, shall we take up where I left off?"

# CHAPTER FOUR

The following morning, which was Sunday, Andrew and I hurried out to find the Rabbi. He was easy to locate because He had become a novelty overnight and everyone was eager to catch a glimpse of this miracle worker.

Throughout the morning, Jesus healed the sick and delivered those who were demon-possessed. Just after noon He stopped beside a merchant's table where He laid His hand on the shoulder of a young man saying, "Come and follow me."

The young man looked up. I was shocked! Tugging on Jesus' sleeve, I whispered, "I know him—that's Philip! Andrew and I grew up with him!"

Philip suddenly and without warning jumped up and shouted, "I will come with you, but I must first go and get my friend!"

Without waiting for a response, he ran off. Jesus appeared to be delighted by his response and sat down on a stack of hay. Ever curious, I decided to follow Philip who did not stop until he came upon a clearing just on the outskirts of the village. Sitting under the widespread branches of a fig tree was a young man on his knees, his face lifted toward heaven.

Philip rushed up, fell down before him and exclaimed, "Nathanael, come! I have found the One who Moses and the Prophets wrote about!

His name is Jesus, the son of Joseph, and He is from Nazareth."

Nathanael laughed and said, "Can any good thing come out of Nazareth?"

Philip answered, "Come and see for yourself!"

As Philip practically dragged Nathanael to his feet, I returned to the Teacher's side, eager to see what was about to happen.

I heard Philip's voice before I could see him. He ran toward Jesus shouting, "Rabbi, I am coming!"

Nathanael followed at a much more reasonable pace.

Jesus was clearly enjoying this.

Philip, completely out of breath and very excited, ran directly up to Jesus. At which point Jesus stood, pointed at Nathanael who was still a ways off and shouted, "Behold, an Israelite indeed, in whom is no bitterness!"

Nathanael came to a complete stop. I sat upright.

*He knows his name!*

Looking around, Nathanael started walking again; the look on his face was one of both uncertainty and anticipation. Jesus walked towards him. With furrowed brow Nathanael asked, "How do You know me?"

Jesus answered, "Before Philip called you, when you were under the fig tree, I saw you."

Nathanael stepped back, his mouth fell open and the color drained from his face. He swallowed hard. Looking into the eyes of the Teacher he exclaimed, "Rabbi, you *are* the Son of God! You *are* the King of Israel!"

Jesus softly laughed. "Do you believe that I am the Son of God because I said that I saw you under the fig tree?"

Nathaniel nodded as he answered, "Yes."

Jesus laid His hand on Nathaniel's arm and said, "Oh, Nathanael, you will see much greater things than these! Truly, truly, I say to you, you shall see the heavens opened and the angels of God ascending and descending on the Son of Man!"[14]

*What kind of talk is this?*

With a nod and a smile, Jesus then walked away. Andrew, Philip,

Nathanael and I hurried after Him, not exactly sure why but certain of one thing, and that was we needed to know more. There was something very wonderful about this Rabbi of Israel.

For the next two days, Andrew and I would fish at night, sleep a few hours and then hurry off to hear Jesus. I was quickly becoming quite fascinated with this Man and His kind ways. I found myself thinking of nothing but the Teacher and desiring to do nothing more than sit in His presence.

On Wednesday, my wife, Miriam, my brother, Andrew and I left for a wedding in Cana. Nathanael lived in Cana and had invited Jesus and us to stay in his home while we were there. I was excited about the prospect of having seven whole days with Jesus.

We crossed the valley and came upon Cana, which was built on the slope of a hill. Just outside the town was a fountain of crystal clear water surrounded by lush gardens and numerous pomegranate orchards. My mouth began to water because Cana was known for having the best pomegranates in all of Palestine.

When we arrived at the wedding, the house was already filled with guests, both old and young. Servants washed our feet. Then we were escorted through the court into the spacious, lofty dining area. Beautiful, festive decorations filled the place. Numerous servants were running here and there with platters of delicious smelling food while musicians played, people danced and everyone celebrated!

We crossed the room to the ceremonial water pots where we washed before eating and then joined the others on cushions around circular tables. I quickly searched the room until I located Jesus; He was sitting with Nathanael and a woman who I learned was His mother.

Later in the evening, after having thoroughly exhausted myself dancing with my beautiful wife, Andrew and I joined James and John at the Teacher's side. We shared fishing stories as Jesus sat with His arm draped across His mother's shoulders. Miriam soon joined us and graciously listened to my stories as if she was hearing them for the first time.

Hearing a slight disturbance behind us, Mary left the table. She returned and said to Jesus, "They have run out of wine."

Jesus tenderly responded, "What does that have to do with us?" Laying His hand on her arm He added, "My hour has not yet come."

Mary's face clearly showed her confusion. Jesus continued, "Mother, there will be a day when I will provide the wine for My wedding guests, but that hour has not yet come."

With a nod Mary turned to the servants and said, "Whatever He says to you, do it."

Jesus pointed to the wall and said, "Fill the pots used for purification with water."

Quite perplexed, the servants simply looked at each other. The head servant motioned for them to comply. With a nod, they filled each one. At which point Jesus said, "Draw some out now and take it to the master of ceremonies."

One of the servants dipped a ladle into the waterpot then poured it into a pitcher. I could not believe my eyes—instead of water it was wine, beautiful red wine! I hurried over for a closer look; Miriam, Andrew, James and John were right behind me.

Every one of the waterpots, all six of them, were filled to the brim with wine!

*How could this have happened?*

Leaning against the wall, I looked at Jesus who watched, smiling that wonderful smile of His.

*How did He do this?*

The servants were just as astonished as we were. They stared at each other as fear filled their eyes. Jesus walked over and put His arm around the servant still holding the ladle and said, "Do not be afraid, my friend. Take the wine to the master of ceremonies."

With a nod, he filled a pitcher and then hurried off. Filling a goblet, he then handed it to the headmaster. We watched with great anticipation. The headmaster tasted the wine and then took another and another. Holding out his goblet for more, the headmaster called the bride and bridegroom to his side. Raising his cup to them he said, "Every man serves the good wine first and when the people have drunk freely, then he serves the poorer wine; but not so with you! You have saved the best wine for last!"

I looked at the Teacher. He was looking into the eyes of His mother speaking ever so quietly to her. I left them to their conversation and hurried off to join everyone in tasting this miraculous wine.[15]

We remained in Cana for the traditional seven days of celebration. Then Andrew, Miriam and I, along with Nathanael, James, John and Philip followed Jesus, His mother and His brothers to Capernaum.[16]

Capernaum is my hometown, a fertile country beside the sea of Galilee. It is called the Garden of Princes because of its lush gardens and beautiful scenery. Just to the north, in clear sight, is the snow-capped Mount Hermon.

Because the Passover was at hand, we remained in Capernaum only two days, long enough for Jesus to invite a young man named Thomas to be one of His disciples.

'Tis a strange thing for Jesus to choose His own disciples, for it was not the custom of rabbis to choose their disciples, but rather the disciples themselves would select who they wanted as their rabbi.

I soon learned that Jesus did nothing because of tradition or custom. He had a completely different method of determining His actions, but it would be nearly a year before I understood that He did what He did because His Father willed it.

It was now April. Upon arriving in Jerusalem, the holy city, John led us to his modest home where we stayed in his guest chamber on the roof. The week preceding the Feast, Jesus spent teaching and healing many. His fame spread like wildfire, and many believed on His name.

On the eve of the 14th, when every head of his family cleansed his home of all leaven and burned it, Jesus entered the temple to do the same, symbolically speaking that is.

Upon entering its courts, a group of men recognized Him and spread the word that the Rabbi was in the temple. By the time we had entered the court of the Gentiles, Jesus had quite a following. It was there that Jesus came to a sudden stop. His piercing eyes took in the scene.

As usual, the place was bustling with activity as pilgrims from both far and near hurried to purchase their animals used for sacrifice.

Once purchased, they then led or carried them to the temple officials for inspection because only a flawless animal would be accepted.

In an effort to secure their business, money changers shouted to the people. Others weighed coins, argued, disputed and bargained with the pilgrims who had to exchange their foreign coins for the half-shekels of the Sanctuary or for ordinary Galilean shekels. I was very familiar with this enterprise. I knew all too well the dishonest transactions that happened here, including the taking advantage of the poor and the widows.

It was not only the hustle and bustle of the people that created such chaos, but also the various noises made by the oxen, sheep, doves and pigeons. The animals added their unique smells to those of the many pilgrims who had traveled for days. The court of the Gentiles was an active, lucrative place of enterprise and anything but peaceful.

Jesus stepped away; I followed closely behind.

Finding some discarded cords near the sheep pen, He chose three and quickly braided them together.

*What did He have on His mind?*

With eyes that were filled with passion, He marched into the very center of the room where He turned to face the money changers' tables and shouted, "Get these things out of here! Stop making My Father's house a house of merchandise!"

In a flash, He laid hold of a table and turned it over. Coins flew through the air, and the money changers scrambled to escape. Jesus did not stop until every one of their tables laid on their sides.

All movement ceased as silence settled on the place like snow falls on the ground.

The money changers, suddenly realizing that their fortunes lay scattered on the temple floor, scrambled to their feet. Jesus cracked His whip; they froze. Tears glistened on His eyelashes as He cried out, "My Father's house is not a house of merchandise!"

I watched in both horror and wonder as He drove both the money changers and the animals out of the temple like a shepherd drives predators away from his sheep.

Zeal for the temple consumed Him.[17]

The Pharisees, who looked on, did nothing. In their heart of hearts, they must have known that He spoke truth.

I looked around at the people. We all knew His actions were justified. I could see respect for the Master in their eyes. Not that He sought it; Jesus never sought man's approval. It was obvious that Jesus just gained a new level of admiration with the common people. I am certain they would have cheered had it not been for the angry glares of the Pharisees.

With tears streaming down His face, He walked directly in front of the temple officials who dared not, out of fear of the crowd, raise a hand. We hurried to follow.

I trembled from a mixture of fear and excitement—fear that the Pharisees would send the guards to arrest Jesus and us because of our association with Him and excitement because I had never seen anyone do what He just did!

James, John, Andrew and I hurried after Jesus who led us to a garden where He stopped to pray. Not sure what to do, we quietly watched from a distance. I soon fell asleep. I woke to the sound of Jesus' singing. John quickly pulled out his flute and joined in. With my head leaning against a tree, I watched as Jesus sang and danced and rejoiced.

Shortly thereafter, we walked the short distance to John's house where we were to eat the main Sabbath meal at noon. Word had quickly spread about Jesus' cleansing the temple and by the time we arrived, the house was buzzing with the news. Jesus was a hero.

The day passed quickly, and with the setting of the sun, we retired to the roof where we spread out our mats under the clear night sky.

Sometime in the night, I woke to the sound of whispering. Rubbing my eyes, I was surprised and shocked to see Nicodemus, a well-known Pharisee and member of the Jerusalem Sanhedrin, completely engrossed in conversation with Jesus. An oil lamp burned brightly on the table between them.

*What is he doing here? Why would a member of the Sanhedrin seek out a Galilean, especially One who is untrained in the Law? I cannot imagine the struggle he most certainly must have had in making the decision to come, for he would have had to have overcome many prejudices and major obstacles in his heart and mind. Not only that, but should his peers discover that he was here it would be extremely detrimental to his career as a Pharisee. This man is either very brave, very desperate or very foolish.*

I leaned forward.

Nicodemus whispered, "Rabbi, we know that You have come from God as a teacher; for no one can do the signs that You do unless God is with him."

*Nicodemus is acknowledging that Jesus has come from God! Unbelievable!*

"Truly, truly, I say to you, unless one is born again, he cannot see the Kingdom of God," Jesus responds.

*Jesus completely ignored what Nicodemus said! He made no reference to it, nor did He expound on it. Instead, He completely changed the subject! This is not very good strategy on Jesus' part. This is the perfect opportunity to get in good with the Pharisees. Jesus knows that Nicodemus is an important man; everyone knows that. It would be in Jesus' best interest to recruit him to be one of His followers. It would certainly be a real boost to His popularity and give Him enormous clout.*

The elderly man responded, "How can a man be born when he is old? He cannot enter a second time into his mother's womb and be born, can he?"

Jesus answered, "Truly, truly, I say to you, unless one is born of water and the Spirit, he cannot enter into the Kingdom of God. That which is born of the flesh is flesh, and that which is born of the Spirit is spirit. Do not marvel that I said to you, 'You must be born again.'"

"What is this that You say?" Nicodemus asked as a sudden gust of wind threatened to blow out the lamp.

Cupping His hands around the small lamp, Jesus continued, "The wind blows where it wishes. You hear the sound of it, but do not know where it comes from or where it is going; so is everyone who is born of the Spirit."

Nicodemus answered, "How can these things be?"

"Oh, Nicodemus," Jesus replied laying His hand on his arm, "are you the teacher of Israel and do not understand these things?

"Truly, truly, I say to you, We speak that which We know, and bear witness of that which We have seen; and you do not receive Our witness. If I told you earthly things and you do not believe, how shall you believe if I tell you heavenly things?"

Nicodemus leaned closer. Jesus continued, "No one has ascended into heaven, but He who descended from heaven, even the Son of Man. And as Moses lifted up the serpent in the wilderness, even so must the Son of Man be lifted up; that whoever believes may in Him have eternal life."

*What is this talk? Is not salvation for the Jews alone?*

Jesus glanced my way and smiled saying, "For God so loved the world, that He gave His only begotten Son, that *whosoever* believes in Him should not perish, but have eternal life.

"For God did not send His Son into the world to judge the world, but that the world should be saved through Him. He who believes in Him is not judged; he who does not believe has been judged already, because he has not believed in the name of the only begotten Son of God.

"And this is the judgment—the Light is come into the world and men loved the darkness rather than the Light; for their deeds were evil.

"For everyone who does evil hates the Light and does not come to the Light, lest his deeds should be exposed. But he who practices the truth comes to the Light, that his deeds may be manifested as having been wrought in God."[18]

Nicodemus sat in silence for a very long time. All around was dark, save the Lamp burning before him. I was certain that Jesus' words were as foreign and unintelligible to Nicodemus as they were to me at that time. You see, Judaism could understand a new relationship with God and man, and even the forgiveness of sins, but it had no concept of a spiritual rebirth. Perhaps, Nicodemus understood in part what entrance into the Kingdom meant, but how one entered that Kingdom was certainly a great mystery to him just as it was to me.

And so it was, Nicodemus bid Jesus good-night and then quickly slipped away under the cover of darkness.

The following day, we left Jerusalem and traveled to the land of Judea where we stopped just south of where John was baptizing. Jesus' followers were large in number, and He immediately began teaching them about baptism. Many believed His words, and Jesus instructed us to baptize them, which we did.

Several days later, Andrew and I visited our old friend, John the baptizer. We found him sitting on a rock by the river bank, alone. He looked heavenward; his whispered words were heard by only One.

Seeing him so engaged, we waited nearby. After some time, John noticed us and shouted, "Andrew! Simon! How good to see you!"

He joined us under the shade of a rather large fig tree. "It is good to see you, John," I said.

"Pray tell me that you still follow the Master," he asked as he leaned towards us, his eyebrows raised.

"Have no fear, we still follow the Teacher," I answered tossing a pebble into the water.

While Andrew told John about Jesus' cleansing the temple, I looked closely at this man. John could not be more than thirty-five years old, yet he looked more like he was fifty. He looked weary, yet peaceful.

After a wonderful visit, we hurried back to Jesus. Along the way, I said, "Andrew, never have I seen John more humble or more self-denying. He seemed almost sad, yet so full of hope!"

"I know. I saw it too."

Two days later, several men joined us. Sitting around the campfire they related their story. They reported that they were disciples of John, and on that very morning, they approached John the baptizer and said, "Rabbi, the Man you endorsed is baptizing people! You should see the crowds surrounding Him! Everyone is going to Him instead of you!"

John answered them, "No one can receive anything if heaven has not given it to him. You know that I told the truth when I said that I was not the Messiah! I am merely one who has been sent ahead of Him to prepare His way. The Bridegroom is the One who will get the Bride. The friend of the Bridegroom is the one who stands by and listens and is thoroughly content to hear the Bridegroom's voice, for His voice makes me glad.

"My friends, this is my joy; it is now complete. Jesus must be the One who is most important. He must *increase* and I *must* decrease. He who comes from above is above all. He who is of the earth is from the earth and speaks of the earth. He who comes from heaven is above all.

"What He has seen and heard, of that He bears witness; and no man receives His witness. He who has received His witness has set his seal to this, that God is true. For He whom God has sent speaks the words of God; for He gives the Spirit without measure. The Father loves the Son, and has given all things into His hand. He who believes in the Son has eternal life; but he who does not obey the Son shall not see life, but the wrath of God abides on him."[19]

John's disciples told us that they trembled in their sandals as he spoke.

The following morning, news came that the Pharisees had heard a report that Jesus was making and baptizing more disciples than John. Jesus responded by leading us out of Judea and into Galilee. Surprisingly, He led us through Samaria where, hungry and weary, He stopped at Jacob's well. He shocked us all by talking to a Samaritan woman. Not only did He talk to her, but He treated her with kindness and respect. He even revealed her deepest secrets, one of which was that she was living with a man that was not her husband.

A Jewish man, especially a rabbi, would never talk to a woman and certainly not a dreadful Samaritan woman, but out of respect, none of us dared to question Him.

After a lengthy discussion, the woman ran into the city telling everyone that she had found the Savior of the world! As a result, many Samaritans came out to speak with Him, begging Him to stay with them, and surprisingly, He did so. Two days later, we left. Many in that city came to believe that He was indeed the Messiah.

Jesus then continued on to Galilee. Andrew and I did not follow since we had to return to our fishing business. We later heard from John that when they arrived in Cana one of Herod's Antipas' officers came to Jesus and pleaded for Him to come to Capernaum and heal his son. Jesus responded, "Unless you see signs and wonders, you simply will not believe."

The officer, ignoring His statement, pleaded, "Sir, come down before my child dies!"

Jesus paused then responded, "Go in peace, for your son will be restored to his health."

The man stared at Jesus for a long moment then said, "I believe."

The following day, that father sent word that his son was indeed alive; the fever had left him at the very time Jesus had said that he would be healed. As a result, the officer and his whole household believed in Jesus.

That was the second sign that Jesus did when He came out of Judea and into Galilee.[20]

## CHAPTER FIVE

Justus interrupts, "Peter, are you saying that Jesus healed that boy without going to him, without even seeing him?"

"That is exactly what He did."

"But that is impossible!" Justus exclaims.

"For men that is impossible, but I learned really quickly that there is nothing impossible for Jesus. He did things that no one had ever done as you have already heard," I answer.

"I can hardly believe what you say, Peter, " Laban adds.

"I can understand your difficulty. I, too, struggled to believe at first. I saw Jesus perform so many miracles that, I suppose, if someone were to write them down the world itself could not contain them."[21]

"I would like to see a miracle," Justus states.

"The greatest miracle of all is the saving of a soul. There is nothing better than that, for that miracle endures through all eternity. Miracles of healing, provision and divine intervention will one day fade away, but a soul lives forever!

"That is why it is important for the world to know Jesus. Many believe that because they have embraced a religion that they have found God. I personally know how damaging religion without relationship is—it quickly becomes legalism.

"I was raised to be a good Jew. I went to synagogue and the temple.

I memorized the Law and faithfully listened to the rabbis. I observed the feasts and traditions of the faith, but when the Master came into my life, my world was turned upside down. I realized that I had spent my entire life focused on external things and very little, if any, on the internal issues of my heart. I faithfully observed the rabbinic traditions, but my heart was far from God. I came to understand that it was only Jesus who could save me, not some form or religion, not even animal sacrifices.

"Jesus made it clear that salvation comes from knowing Him personally. Do not think that salvation comes from knowing *about* Him; the demons know about Him and tremble. Neither is about observing rituals and traditions. No, my friends, salvation comes from being in a personal, intimate relationship with the Son of God.

"Jesus was truly amazing. Instead of ignoring and avoiding sinners, He pursued their friendship; He went out of His way to show them kindness. This was completely foreign to me. I had never experienced a religion like that. God came to earth as a Man in order to show us what He and His Father were really like and what They truly desired.

"Jesus' actions were not based on human need, neither were they based on the fear of man. He was unconcerned with gaining the approval of man. He desired the approval of only One and that was His Father.

Jesus marched to the beat of a different drummer, a drummer that played a song that had never been written, heard or seen. A drummer with a beat that would change the world—one person at a time."

# CHAPTER SIX

Jesus spent the next three months, from June to August, teaching in the various synagogues in Galilee.[22] He was, for the most part, unattended since we had all returned to our homes and various occupations.

During that summer, news about Him spread throughout all the surrounding districts. Almost daily, Andrew and I heard reports of His great exploits. His fame was spreading rapidly.

And so it was, on a cool morning in September, I laid down my nets and climbed up on my boat to get a closer look at the Teacher. He walked my way, and the crowd parted. Our eyes met, and to my delight, Jesus shouted, "Simon, My friend!"

My heart beat furiously in response.

*What is it about this Man that fascinates me so? Why is it that every time I am near Him I feel the weight of my sinful nature and yet, at the same time, feel drawn to Him? I have never felt so torn, so challenged, so weak and, at the same time, so compelled as I do in His presence.*

The crowd pressed against Him like thirsty sheep following their shepherd to water. Stopping directly in front of me, Jesus smiled. It felt as though time stood still.

*His eyes contain such depth, such wisdom, such kindness and great authority. Why does He spend His time with men such as I?*

With His hand extended toward my boat, He asked, "May I?"

I nodded.

Wading into the water, Jesus climbed in and then said, "Simon, would you push Me out a little way from the shore?"

Nudging Andrew, I whispered, "Come with us, brother."

"I wouldn't dream of letting you get into that boat without me," he answered.

We threw our nets in, pushed the boat out and then jumped in. When we were only a few feet from the shore, Jesus said, "This is far enough."

We dropped the anchor. Jesus sat in the bow of the boat and preached to the eager crowd.

Sitting in the shadow of the Rabbi, I was once more gripped by the power and authority in which He spoke.

*John the baptizer is a dynamic preacher, unlike anyone I had ever heard, but even John, as great as he is, pales in comparison to Jesus. The Rabbi's message is powerful. It seems as though His power comes from some inner source, from something full of life. I am not exactly sure what it is, I only know that there is a fire within Him that compels me to know Him more, to delve into the depths of His being and drink from His wisdom.*

"Simon. Simon Peter."

I looked up to see that the Teacher had turned around and was calling me. Andrew snickered and shoved me from behind saying, "Were you sleeping in class?"

Ignoring him, I answered, "Yes, Rabbi?"

"Simon, if you will row out to the deep water and let down your nets, you will get a great catch."

I looked back at Andrew who simply shrugged his shoulders. I looked through the clear water to the bottom of the sea.

*What He proposes is crazy.*

Facing the Teacher, I responded, "But Master, Andrew and I fished all night, and we caught absolutely nothing."

His only response was a raised eyebrow.

"You're serious, aren't you?" I asked.

He slowly nodded.

Looking into the Master's steady eyes, I responded, "I do not believe for a moment that we will be successful, but because You say to do so, we will let down the nets."

Andrew raised the sails while I grabbed the oars and began rowing towards the deep. I looked back at Jesus; His dark eyes scanned the sea.

*Jesus is a great preacher, but He obviously knows very little about fishing. Anyone who knows anything about fishing knows that the best time to fish is at night when it is dark and the fish cannot see us. It is a waste of time to throw a net into the water in the daylight.*

Jesus spoke, "Let down your nets right here."

I dropped the anchor. With one last questioning look at Jesus, Andrew threw his net over one side while I threw mine over the other.

I looked back at the shore. We were close enough that everyone could see what we were doing. Our fishing partners, James and John, stood in their boat watching closely.

*How ridiculous we must look! How foolish I feel!*

Suddenly, a tug on my arm caused me to look into the water. A multitude of fish fought to get into my net! In shocked disbelief, I looked back at Andrew who was also fighting to hold onto his net full of fish. Jesus chuckled saying, "Perhaps, I should give you a hand."

Even with His help, I strained to hold the weighty catch; my net began to break. I looked back at Andrew who looked at me and shouted, "I can't help you! It is all I can do to hold onto mine!"

I shouted to James and John who, having seen our predicament, were already on their way.

Staring into the eyes of the Teacher, I wondered how this happened. *How did He know those fish would be in that exact location?*

James and John arrived just in time and, with their help, we managed to haul in the first net, which was so full that it caused our boat to sink dangerously low in the water. Seeing this, we hauled Andrew's net into James and John's boat.

As Andrew worked on raising the sails, I looked at the Teacher who stood knee-deep in fish. I was a young man then, but I had fished long enough to know that what I had witnessed was a miracle.

Amazed and full of fear, I stood trembling before this One who not only turned water into wine and healed the sick, but also commanded the fish of the sea.

Suddenly I seemed very small and not nearly as important as before.

*Just who is this man? And what does He want with someone like me? I have nothing to offer One so great!*

Fear gripped my heart, and I fell to my knees in the middle of the fish and cried out, "Go away from me, Sir, for I am a sinful man!"

Laying His hand gently on my shoulder Jesus responded, "Simon, don't be afraid! There is no need to send Me away. Do you not know that I came for weak and sinful men?"

I did not know how to respond.

Jesus continued, "Simon, from now on you will be catching men."[23]

I looked up into the kindest eyes I had ever seen—eyes filled with wonder, with grace, with truth, with mercy, with delight, with understanding and most of all—eyes filled with amazing, unending love!

*How could this be? Jesus was undaunted by my confession and my sinful nature. He invited me, even in my weakness, to remain with Him! I could not understand such thinking, such mercy!*

He continued, "Simon, when you come face to face with your weaknesses and your sinful nature, do not send Me away; do not run from Me. Instead, run to Me. You can be sure that I will accept you; I will never reject you, for I love you even in your weakness and immaturity."

*He loves and accepts me just as I am! What kind of talk is this? No one on earth loves like this!*

Andrew, standing almost knee-deep in fish, interrupted my tumultuous thoughts as he leaned forward and announced, "I do not understand what has happened here today, but there is one thing I see clearly and that is this—we'd better head to shore before we sink."

Reluctantly, I put my hand to the oars. Before we even reached the shore several men waded out to meet us and dragged our boats to the beach.

The crowd erupted in applause. Jesus jumped out of the boat making a large splash, which completely drenched a young boy standing nearby who giggled as water dripped off his little nose. Jesus went to him, swept him up in His arms and spun him around. The boy squealed with delight as his mother timidly looked on.

The crowd kept shouting, slapping us on the back as though we did some heroic thing. For a moment, I was caught up in their praise until I remembered whose miracle this really was. I searched for the Master. He still held the little boy and was whispering something in his ear. The little guy nodded in response. Jesus then placed the boy beside his young mother who quickly turned her eyes away.

The Master leaned forward and quietly spoke to her. Slowly, she lifted her face and met His gaze. He again spoke. She nodded as tears filled her eyes like rain fills a bucket.

Jesus took her small hand in His and looked up to heaven.

*He was praying for her! He was praying for a woman—in public!*

I stepped closer. Tears cascaded down her cheeks falling onto the beach. Her little boy clutched her garment, hugging her knees.

Jesus then wiped her tears with the back of His hand as He quietly spoke to her. His face reflected the pure love He felt.

*I could not believe my eyes! What was He doing? He, being Jewish, certain knew that His behavior went against our customs and traditions! After all, He was born and raised in Israel; He had Jewish parents. He certainly knew the Law, for He quoted it better than any rabbi I knew.*

At this point, Jesus turned His attention to me. I quickly looked away. Jesus then returned to my boat, picked up a fish, looked from me to Andrew then said, "Follow me and I will make you fishers of men."

He hesitated only a moment, tossed the fish back in the boat, and then walked away disappearing into the crowd.

*Fisher of men? What did that mean? Follow Him where? Where will He take me if I follow? Where does this journey end?*

Andrew tugged on my sleeve. I saw the desire in his eyes to become one of Jesus' disciples. I jumped on the bow of the boat and searched the crowd for Jesus, but to no avail; the Master had been swallowed by the mass of people.

*I had no idea where He would take me or what He was talking about, but I did know this—I knew that I could not live without Him. I had seen something in Jesus that I desperately needed.*

I looked back at our boats. They were nearly filled to the rim with fish. There is a lot of money in those fish, I thought.

*We are famous. The crowd thinks we are heroes. Everyone will want to buy our fish. Everyone will be talking about us for months, maybe even years, for nothing like this has ever happened in Israel. We have quite a successful fishing career ahead of us. Why now? Why did the Master ask us to walk away just when things are finally going great? Had he asked me this morning when I was discouraged after a long night of empty nets I would have followed without a second thought, but now?*

His words echoed through my mind, "Follow Me and I will make you fishers of men."

"Okay," I said to no one in particular, "Okay, I will follow You!"

Without saying another word, Andrew and I ran after Him leaving the greatest catch of fish of my life to follow the Master.

We found Jesus a short distance down the beach standing before James and John. He laid His hands on each of their shoulders and said, "Come and follow Me."

Having extended the invitation, offering no comfort, no promise of grandeur and no explanations, Jesus continued on His way leaving the decision with them as He did with Andrew and me.

*This man does not seek to control, neither does He bribe or manipulate people. His has a pure heart with perfect motives.*

My eyes met John's for a moment; I silently urged him to follow. Andrew and I left, knowing that the decision must be completely theirs and knowing that even if they said no, we must leave our beloved partners and friends behind in pursuit of the One who we would come to learn had the answers to our deepest needs and most difficult questions.

Without waiting another moment, Andrew and I hurried after the Master. I looked over my shoulder long enough to see James and John bidding their father good-bye. They quickly caught up to us saying, "We told our father that we're going to be fishers of men."

"And what did he say?" Andrew asked.

"Nothing, he said nothing," James answered.

"I don't think he understood," John added.

"Well, I don't understand either, but hopefully one day I will. One day we all will." I responded.

And so it was that the Master's simple words, cast like a net into the sea, captured not only me, but also my brother and our two fishing partners, James and John. Little did we know that the decision we made that day would one day require all that we were and all that we would ever be. As we followed Him, we came to understand that to be a disciple of Jesus it will cost you everything.

# CHAPTER SEVEN

Justus frantically whispers, "Peter, someone is coming!"

The sound of feet rapidly approaching fills me with dread. In the distance, a prisoner groans loudly. I take the time to pray for him.

A key slowly turns in the lock, and I tuck my face under my arm in an effort to shield my eyes from the blinding light that is sure to come.

*The pain from a torch is minor compared to the pain experienced by those who encounter, upon their death, the Light of the world after rejecting Him.*

Ever so slowly and quietly the door opens and a voice whispers, "Peter, it is I, Tiberias. I have brought medicine, food and water."

"Greetings, my friend. Where is your torch?" I ask as he quietly shuts the door behind him.

"I did not bring it, but I did bring a small lamp," he whispers.

Looking up I reply, "Tiberias, I am so happy to report that I now have two new friends, Justus and Laban. I have been telling them of the Master."

"That is indeed good news," Tiberias responds.

Without wasting another moment, Tiberias quickly and carefully rubs soothing ointment over my face. "This will help with the infection and will keep the insects away," he says.

"It is most appreciated. How is your wife? Did you remember to thank her for the bread?"

"I did, and she was so blessed that she made another loaf and sent some goat cheese for you," he answers.

"Someone's coming!" Laban says.

The unmistakable sound of clanging keys and shuffling feet fill my ears.

*Oh, Lord hide us in the shadow of Your wing and protect my friend and Your servant, Tiberias!*

The key slides into the lock; I hold my breath.

*Intervene now, Lord!*

The door opens only a few inches, hesitates and suddenly slams shut. The sound of feet hurrying away brings great relief. My heart is racing. I whisper a prayer of gratitude and then say, "Tiberias, you must go now, before they return."

Stuffing a piece of cheese in my mouth, Tiberias replies, "Take a drink from my pouch first."

I quickly swallow the cheese then take a long drink. "Thank you again, my friend. Now, you must go!"

He places a piece of the bread in my mouth saying, "I will, but first I must give your new friends some water and bread."

Without waiting for me to respond, he quickly crawls away as Laban and Justus cry out to him. The other prisoners, who I have yet to meet, also cry out for food and water.

"Peter, there are more than two friends in this cell with you," Tiberias states.

"There are indeed, but I have not had the privilege of meeting them," I answer.

"Well, I have food and water enough for all," Tiberias quietly responds.

"You are a good man, Tiberias," I replied.

Once the food and water are gone, Tiberias bids us farewell then quietly makes his way back to the door. I pray for his safe escape. Amazingly, the door does not creak or groan as he opens and closes it.

As his footsteps fade into the distance, I let out a huge sigh of relief.

*He is safe! Thank You, Lord, for helping my friend.*

"That guard has risked his life for not only you, Peter, but also for us. We mean nothing to him. I am a murdering thief, a nobody, a nothing. So, why would he take a chance of getting caught to help the likes of us?" Justus asks.

"He did so because the love of the Father lives in him. You see, love lays down its life for another. Tiberias has surrendered his life to the Lord; he now lives according to the law of love. My friends, once you surrender your life to Jesus and give Him permission to transform you into His image, He begins to change you and remake you. This temporary life does not seem so important any more. What does become important is your relationship with Jesus and with others. His love changes people."

"I have never known a love like that," Justus states.

"Jesus is the true Source of such love; it can only come from Him. A man might love, but to love consistently with no thought to one's own well-being must come from the wellspring of life whose name is Jesus."

"Then tell us more about Jesus. Tell us how He lived His life. I want to know every detail, every event, all that He said and did, for there is a hunger growing within me to know Him!" Justus states.

"I will not leave you uninformed, my friend. I can tell you that I came to know beyond a shadow of a doubt that Jesus of Nazareth surely is the Messiah. I am confident that you will also come to see and understand that He is indeed the chosen One from heaven.

"When I became a follower of Jesus, I was just a young man possessed by a dream, a dream of Rome being conquered by a powerful King who would establish His throne in Jerusalem. I dreamed this dream every day. It compelled me, like my father Abraham, to leave behind everything that I might embrace what probably looked foolish to others, but it turned out to be my salvation and the salvation of the world. My greatest desire is for all of you to know Him and love Him!"

# CHAPTER EIGHT

A ndrew, James, John and I left everything to follow Jesus. After many hours of walking on the dusty road that led from the sea to Capernaum, under a blistering sun, I found myself doubting my decision.

*I want nothing more than a good meal and a good night's sleep. At the pace we're traveling, neither of those things look like they will happen any time soon.*

I stumbled over my feet nearly falling face first. Andrew looked my way but said nothing.

*I wonder if he is regretting his decision, too. I can't believe that the four of us have walked away from our fishing business just when it looked so promising. No more fishing—I love fishing; it is all I have ever known. And what did Jesus mean when He said He'd make us fishers of men? What is that all about?*

*What have I gotten myself into?*

Being so caught up in my thoughts, I had not noticed that Jesus had made His way to my side. Handing me a cluster of grapes, He said, "Peter, I am so very glad you decided to follow Me."

I merely nodded; a lump formed in my throat preventing me from responding. The Master looked hard and long into my eyes. I was certain He saw the emptiness within, the selfish ambition and all my miserable doubts.

*I fished all night and caught nothing—that is exactly how I feel right now—like a big failure.*

Jesus said, "Peter, in My Kingdom, your worth is never based on your performance. It is based on Who I am and how I feel about you. And I think you are wonderful! I love you, My friend."

"You do?"

With a chuckle, He answered, "I certainly do, and I am glad you have chosen to follow Me. That decision was the best decision you will ever make. You see, Peter, I see something within you that you cannot see right now. I see a leader, a rock, a lover. That is who you are, but it will take some years before you walk in the fullness of that. During the process, it is important for you to trust Me, for I desire to mold you and shape you and make you into the image of your heavenly Father. I am faithful to complete that which I have begun."

My doubts suddenly flew away like a bird escaping from a cage. "I am glad I decided to follow You," I responded.

With His arm draped across my shoulder, we continued on, eating our grapes, not saying much, but then nothing more needed to be said.

Once in Capernaum, we went directly to my home where we were welcomed by my lovely wife and mother-in-law. After dinner, everyone retired for the night. Miriam and I, however, went for a walk through the moonlit pasture. "The Rabbi asked me to be one of His disciples today," I said feeling rather proud.

"And what did you say?"

"I said yes," I answered.

We walked on in silence for a few minutes. Fireflies danced all around us. Turtle doves cooed in the distance. It was a beautiful night, a good night.

"Simon," Miriam began to say.

"Jesus calls me Peter," I interrupted.

"He does, does He?" she responded, softly laughing. I have always loved her laugh.

She continued, "Well, you are still Simon to me. There is

something unique about the Rabbi. I don't know what it is, but I know it is real and that it is good. I can not imagine a better Rabbi for you to spend some time with than He."

"Well, that's what I wanted to talk with you about. You see, this Rabbi, like you said, is unlike any other. He does not just want me to spend a few hours with Him, but He asked not only me, but also Andrew, James and John to leave behind our fishing business so that we can spend all our time with Him. It seems that He does not want just a part of me, but all of me."

I held my breath as I waited for her response. It was not that I needed her approval, but because I respected her insights and loved her dearly that I hoped for a positive response.

"Simon, I trust you and I trust the Rabbi. I think that it is wonderful that you said yes. Follow the Master, Peter."

The following morning, which was the Sabbath, we accompanied Jesus to the synagogue where He immediately began to teach. A crowd quickly gathered.

Looking at the sea of faces, it was obvious that they were just as amazed with His teaching as I was. His teaching was filled with passion and kindness. Jesus spoke with amazing wisdom and great zeal.

Suddenly, the quiet, serene atmosphere in the synagogue was interrupted by the sound of low, guttural growling. I searched the crowd until I saw, huddled in a far corner, a wild-looking man. He looked vaguely familiar.

The man bolted upright and leapt like a wild animal into the center of the crowd. Shaking an angry fist in the air, he shouted, "Ha! What business do we have with You, Jesus of Nazareth? Have You come to destroy us?"

His face was grossly contorted and his body shook violently. Foamy saliva fell from his chin as he spewed out, "I know who You are! You are the holy One of God!"

With a calm, yet firm voice Jesus took authority over the unclean spirit and said, "Be quiet and come out of him!"

The evil spirit immediately threw the man on the ground then, with a final shriek, the demon left. Peace quickly settled over the man's frame. He stood, brushing the dust from his tunic and then took his seat as though nothing had happened.[24]

It was then that I realized that I knew him. This man was one of our regular customers. Through the years, he has bought many fish from us, but I had no idea that he was demon-possessed!

As discreetly as possible, I made my way to his side. Whispering, I asked, "Matthias, how do you feel?'

"Free, brother. For the first time in my life, I feel free!"

"Well, you look ten years younger," I said throwing my arm around his shoulder.

"I think I might be," he answered.

The crowd that had witnessed Matthias' deliverance was suddenly on their feet. Their whisperings sounded much like a swarm of bees. A debate quickly broke out. One of the religious leaders shouted out, "What kind of message is this that we have not only heard, but have also seen demonstrated before our very eyes this day?"

Another jumped to his feet and responded, "As for the message, I do not know, but I can say that with authority and power this Man commands unclean spirits and they come out!"

An elderly man added, "Never have we seen such power and authority in this city!"

"This is not real; it is a trick!" shouted another.

The debate quickly escalated. Without responding, Jesus quietly slipped out; we followed. I pushed close to the Master hoping that He would have something to say, but He did not.

Seeing that it was nearly noon, we hurried home for the Sabbath meal. Excitedly, I led the way through the streets. And all along the way, the people buzzed with the news of Matthias' deliverance.

As we entered my house, Miriam met us with the news that her mother was in bed with what we call the Burning Fever. I knew what the rabbis instructed to be done: one must take a knife made entirely of iron and tie it with a braid of hair to a thorn bush. This was to be done for several days, and then the bush was to be cut down while a particular phrase was spoken at which point the cure was suppose to follow.[25]

I looked to Jesus and said, "Master, we just saw you set a man free who was possessed by an evil spirit. You have power and authority unlike anything I have ever seen. Would You exercise that same power and heal my mother-in-law from this fever?"

Jesus answered, "Take Me to her."

Like a litter of eager, hungry puppies, we followed the Master as He entered my mother-in-law's room. Jesus stood over her for a brief moment then, ignoring the rabbis' instructions, He took her hand in His and rebuked the fever. The fever left her just as quickly as that evil spirit left Matthias. With great joy, she sat up and thanked Him. She then hurried to the kitchen to help with the final meal preparations.

As we reclined around the table, I found myself deep in thought.

*What did I just see? The rabbis were clear as to how to cure the Burning Fever, but Jesus completely disregarded these instructions. With a touch of His hand, my mother-in-law was cured! Just who is this Man who wields such power and reclines at my table? That is the question that continually races through my mind. Just who is He?*

Throughout the meal, the Master paid close attention to everyone, including women and children. He delighted in telling stories with hidden meanings. He was indeed a wonderful and delightful guest.

Jesus stood beckoning us to follow. He opened my front door and what I saw completely shocked me, to put it mildly. My yard and the street leading to the market place were filled with people; some stood, while others sat. The sick, lying on pallets, lined the streets.

The sun set and, one by one, the stars came out marking the end of the Sabbath. Jesus turned to me and said, "For God so loved the world...." He then hurried out to meet them; we eagerly followed. Jesus moved among the people healing the sick and setting free those possessed by evil spirits. There was no one too sick to be healed. He cast out evil spirits and when they tried to speak, He immediately silenced them saying, "Be quiet, it is not time for my identity to be made known."[26]

I was amazed and in awe of His power.

It was well after the moon had passed overhead when Jesus turned to me and said, "Now, it is time for us to rest."

We made our way back inside. My wife, Miriam and my mother-in-law had long since gone to bed. I led the Master and His other disciples to the rooftop where they spread out their pallets.

Bidding them good-night, I joined my wife who woke only long enough to say, "Today, I met a King!"

My body was exhausted, but my mind was racing.

*What a day this was! The miraculous deeds that Jesus did today cannot be concealed nor kept secret. Jesus has certainly become a threat to the Pharisees, but to the common man and woman He is quickly becoming their hero. Never has Jesus appeared more glorious as He did tonight under the starlit sky, moving through the suffering multitude healing both body and soul.*

A sound woke me; it was still dark. I looked up just in time to see the Master slip quietly out the door.

*Where is He going at such an early hour?*

Exhausted, I quickly drifted back to sleep.

Just outside my window, a rooster crowed. Throwing off my blanket, I stumbled to the basin to wash my face. The cool water helped to wake me. Remembering that Jesus had slipped out during the night, I hurried up the stairs. John and Andrew were engrossed in conversation; the others still slept. Seeing me, John asked, "Do you know where the Master has gone?"

"He left while it was still dark," I answered.

Andrew jumped up asking, "But, where did He go?"

"I don't know, but I am going to look for Him," I answered already headed down the stairs. John and Andrew quickly followed.

We grabbed our tunics; I threw open the front door and stopped so suddenly that Andrew slammed into me, which caused John to crash into him. The three of us stood smashed together in the doorway, our mouths open and our eyes wide with wonder. As far as eye could see, the yard was covered with sleeping bodies.

My home was built on a ridge with a large, wide, open space before it. From every direction, people were streaming in from the surrounding districts.

As we carefully stepped over and through the vast sea of desperate people, they continually asked us where the Healer was.

A wave of pride swept through me as I thought about the fact that this Rabbi, who is able to heal the sick and cleanse the lepers and cast out demons, slept in my house and ate at my table.

Once we made it through the crowd, we headed for a grove of trees. "This is where I go when I want to be alone," I said.

"I know," my brother replied, "Have you forgotten how many times I found you here?"

Ignoring him, I took the lead. After a short hike, we found the Teacher in a small clearing among a grove of trees. He knelt against a large stone; His eyes raised to heaven.

"Teacher, everyone is looking for You," I announced. He slightly nodded acknowledging me. I looked at Andrew and James who merely shrugged.

I tried again, "Teacher, everyone is looking for You. It appears that the miracle You did in the temple has caused You to become quite popular. People from every direction are flocking to my house as we speak. You must come with us, for the needs are great!"

He answered my plea by inviting us to sit with Him on the thick grass. Andrew and John joined Him, but I remained standing, eager to get back to the crowd where I knew miracles would happen, and we would become famous.

Jesus looked up at me and said, "Simon, I dare not respond to either the need or the demand. Neither do I respond to the temptation to become popular. I do what I do because My Father tells Me to. I do only what I see Him doing, nothing more and nothing less."

As He so often did, He looked long and hard into my eyes for an uncomfortable amount of time then continued, "Come, let us go elsewhere. Let us go to the nearby villages so I can preach there also, for that is why I came."[27]

At the time, I did not understand how He could walk away from such a wonderful opportunity and from so many in need, but later I understood.

We spent many weeks traveling throughout Galilee where Jesus preached the good news of the Kingdom and healed the sick. I felt as though I was learning for the first time what it really meant to serve God. Listening to the Master, I realized that the good news was so much more than the Law, it was truth, the truth of what God is really like and how He feels about us. The message that Jesus delivered brought hope to the hopeless and revealed the path to eternal life not just for Jews, but also for Gentiles.

Not only was His message life-changing, but the way He related to the people was unlike anything we had ever seen. What great pains He took in ministering! He was extremely gracious and ever so patient with the crowds. He cured their sicknesses, their diseases and all their torments. No one was beyond His reach, not even the worst of sinners. No sickness was too difficult for Jesus to heal with simply a word or a touch. The more I saw, the more amazed and intrigued I became with this Man.

Everywhere we went, in every village, town and city, the people were very fond of the Master. Even though Jesus had chosen a solitary place like Galilee to be His mission field, people came from as far away as Decapolis, Jerusalem, Judea and even beyond the Jordan to hear Him.[28]

Because every day was filled with new adventures and great wonders, the days passed ever so quickly. Five weeks had gone by when my wife and I were laying under the stars reflecting on the events of the day. Nearby, the Master and other disciples slept. A nearby owl randomly called out, "Who, who?"

Laughing I answered, "I know who—it's Jesus of Nazareth, that's who."

Miriam giggled; she had such a delightful laugh. I so loved to hear it.

*My father chose well when he chose this one to be my bride.*

I ran my fingers through her jet black hair that shone like glass under the light of the moon.

*What a blessed man I am! I have the most beautiful and wonderful wife in the world. And, if that's not good enough, the greatest Teacher who has ever lived has chosen me to be His disciple, a Teacher who can perform miracles. I am indeed a blessed man!*

"Miriam," I said, "Jesus reminds me of the moon."

"Are you saying He's round?" she replied quietly laughing.

"Don't try to be funny, my love. It is because He is bringing light to a dark world that I say He is like the moon."

"Simon, that is true, but if I were to compare Him to anything it would be to the sun, not the moon," she responded propping herself up on her elbow. "After all, the sun is the greater of the two lights. The sun completely drives away the darkness whereas the moon merely provides light in midst of darkness. And the sun never changes, but the moon grows darker with each passing day until there is nothing left.

"No, Simon, I would not compare the Master to the moon, but I would compare people to the moon because we are always changing, sometimes doing good, other times failing miserably. Sometimes we shine brightly, sometimes we shine dimly and then there are those who never shine at all."[29]

"You are so brilliant! That's why I married you!" I responded.

"I suppose it had nothing to do with my beautiful face or my great personality or the fact that your father saw something in me that he felt would help balance out his sometimes overly zealous son?"

"Of course not!" I answered laughing.

"Simon, you are impossible, but I love you dearly!"

I soon fell asleep and dreamed of the Master riding into Jerusalem on a white horse. With His sword raised, He slayed the Romans and then ascended to the throne.

It was not yet light when I woke. I heard movement nearby and looked up just in time to see the Master slipping away into the darkness. After trying to go back to sleep and finding it impossible, I decided to see if I could find Him. Having grown up in this area, I had a good idea where He might go. There was a cleft in the rock on the side of the hill not far from here; it was a perfect place to hide away.

The moonlight illumined my path as I made my way through the lush vegetation. I had traveled about halfway up the hillside when I saw the Master a short distance away. He was right where I thought He would be doing exactly what I thought He would be doing. The light from the moon streamed into the small opening highlighting His frame.

He was on His knees, His prayer shawl covered His head and His face was buried in His hands. I continued on until I was standing just this side of the mouth of the cave. From the shaking of His shoulders, it appeared that the Master was crying.

I turned away.

"Simon Peter, come and join Me," He said. His voice was filled with longing and gentleness, even more than normal.

Somewhat reluctant, I entered the cave and sat on the large stone He knelt against. "I did not mean to intrude or interrupt. I was unable to sleep and thought that I might find You here."

"Peter, you are always welcome to come to Me," He said wiping His face on His shawl.

*From the looks of that shawl, it has been used to wipe thousands of tears. Never have I known a Man with so much joy and, at the same time, so many tears.*

"This country is quite pleasant to the soul, is it not?" Jesus asked.

"Truthfully, I haven't really noticed," I answered as I wiped the sweat from my forehead. A welcome breeze made its way into our little cave.

Looking out at the rolling, green hills littered with rocks of various sizes, I responded, "Everyone looks down on Galilee. It is such a remote part of Israel and is considered rude and boorish. The people of these parts are considered good enough to be soldiers or fishermen, but not good enough to be scholars or men of any honorable reputation. Why, even our language is considered simple. So, Master, I do not think that I would call this country pleasant, neither would I say that we are a desirable people."

Picking up a small stone and tossing it, I continued, "So, why have You chosen a place like Capernaum to be Your home? Why not stay in Your home town of Nazareth? After all, Nazareth is a great city, and it certainly has a better reputation than this place."

Jesus answered, "Peter, before I called you, I taught in the synagogue in Nazareth. It was the Sabbath morning, and the officials were all assembled. Having heard reports of the wonders done in

Cana and Capernaum, the chief ruler requested that I be the appointed messenger of the congregation for the day."

"They asked You to be the One who read the portion from the Prophets and conducted the devotions?" I asked somewhat surprised since that is a position of great honor.

Softly laughing, He responded, "It is true. I stood at the lectern and began with the traditional prayer: 'Blessed be Thou, O Lord, King of the world, Who formed the light and created the darkness, Who made peace, and created everything. Who, in mercy, gives light to the earth, and to those who dwell upon it, and in Thy goodness, day by day, and every day, renews the works of creation. Blessed be the Lord our God for the glory of His handiworks, and for the light-giving lights which He has made for His praise. Selah. Blessed be the Lord our God, Who has formed the lights.'[30]

"I then led them in the second prayer. Next, I was followed by the priest, Levite and, in succession, five Israelites who read from the Law. It was then My turn to read the concluding portion of Scripture. Standing before the congregation, I was handed the scroll and turning to this passage in Isaiah, read, 'The Spirit of the Lord is upon Me, because He appointed Me to preach the gospel to the poor. He has sent Me to proclaim release to the captives, and recovery of sight to the blind, to set free those who are downtrodden, to proclaim the favorable year of the Lord.'

"Then, I preached. I spoke of hope and promises, of repentance and My Father's Kingdom. I closed the scroll, handed it back to the attendant and then sat down. The eyes of all the people in the synagogue were fixed upon Me. It was obvious that they were receptive to My message. I stood back up and added, 'Today, this Scripture has been fulfilled in your hearing.'

"The people were speaking well of Me and were wondering at My gracious words. I could hear them saying, 'Is this not Joseph's son? Is not Mary His mother? And do not His sisters still live in this town?'

"They were clearly amazed that I, a simple carpenter's son, would speak such words of life. And then, it happened. I stood back up and said, 'No doubt you will quote this proverb to Me, 'Physician heal yourself! Whatever we heard was done at Capernaum, do here in Your home town as well.'

"I responded, 'Truly I say to you, no prophet is welcome in his home town. But I say to you in truth, there were many widows in Israel in the days of Elijah when the sky was shut up for three and a half years and a great famine came over all the land. And yet Elijah was sent to help none of them, but only to Zarephath, in the land of Sidon, to a Gentile woman who was a widow. And there were many lepers in Israel in the time of Elisha the prophet, but none of them was cleansed except a Gentile by the name of Naaman.'

"Hearing these words everyone was filled with rage. They rose up and threw Me out of the synagogue pushing and shoving Me to the brow of the hill on which the city had been built. They planned to press against Me until I fell over the forty foot cliff."

"You see, Peter, it was not My message that caused them to be offended with Me, but it was the fact that the One who spoke was viewed as nothing more than the son of a carpenter who had grown up in their midst. Had someone important spoken the same words, they would not have taken such extreme action against him."

"One man against a city. How did you escape?" I asked.

"I escaped because it was not My time; I simply walked away, through the midst of them. I left that day and came here, to Capernaum, a meek and lowly city."[31]

"I am sorry they rejected You."

"Peter, I love the people of My hometown, and I long for them to know the truth, but many do not have ears to hear or eyes to see. It is a great mystery, Peter, but no prophet is welcome in his hometown, not even Me."

"I do not understand how anyone could reject You. It makes no sense."

"I am dealing with so much more than you know, Peter. But that topic is for another day, another time." Jesus stood and said, "Now come, let us join the others, for the day is breaking and My Father has much planned."

# CHAPTER NINE

Justus interrupts, "Peter, I don't understand. If Jesus was the Son of God then how could the people He grew up with reject Him?"

"That was part of the problem, my friend. They knew His mother and His earthly father. They knew that His parents were just simple people, common laborers. And they watched Jesus grow up. They saw Him laugh and cry, eat and sleep, play and work just like all of the other children. They sat beside Him in the synagogue and were present at His bar mitzvah. To them, He was no different from every other boy in Nazareth.

"So, when Jesus announced that He had come to set free those in bondage and proclaim the good news to the poor, the people were offended and insulted. They were unable to even consider that He might be the answer to their prayers for a Deliverer, a Messiah.

"Their preconceived ideas became a stumbling block, and they closed their minds refusing to even listen to His words of life. You see, my friends, jealousy, fear and ignorance blind the heart and stop up the ears."

"Peter, I have lived my whole life that way. I refused to listen to anyone," Laban answers.

"As have I," Justus adds.

"But, that is no longer true, my friends, for you have chosen to hear about the One who has eternal life. God always feeds a hungry heart. All you have to do is ask the Father to draw you close and He does, for every good and perfect gift comes from Him and should flow back to Him."[32]

# CHAPTER TEN

After hearing about Jesus' rejection by His hometown, Jesus and I left the cave and headed back to the others. He appeared to be in no hurry, which was a real challenge for me because I was always in a hurry. Jesus drew my attention to things I rarely noticed, things like a mother fox with her newly born pups nestled in the hollow of a tree stump, a patch of wildflowers dancing in the wind and a beautiful, white dove sitting on her nest as her mate watches closely on the branch of a nearby olive tree.

*Is there anything that He does not enjoy?*

"Sin," the Master stated.

"Excuse me?" I asked puzzled.

"Peter, there is one thing I find no pleasure in and that is sin. Sin destroys, which is contrary to the nature of God. Sin opposes Me and keeps those I love in bondage and in pain and far from Me. I do not take pleasure in things which destroy those that I love so dearly."

*The Master knew what I was thinking! How is that possible?*

"There is nothing impossible for Me, absolutely nothing," He continued.

*He did it again.*

I desperately tried to clear my mind of any thoughts. Jesus stopped, turned around and, with eyes that appeared to be dancing,

He laughed.

*He is enjoying this!*

Placing His arm around my shoulder, He said, "Simon Peter, there is nothing that I do not know either on this earth or in the one to come. I enjoy you. You are a delight to Me."

*Is this man safe? After all, He knows my thoughts!*

"Your secrets are safe with Me," He answered.

We continued on and soon rejoined Andrew, James, John, Philip, Nathanael and Thomas who were still sleeping. The women were busy preparing bread. I rolled up my pallet, keeping one eye on the Master who stood watching the sleeping disciples. His look was one filled with great affection.

*Something is going on.*

Stuffing my pallet in my basket, I quietly joined the Master placing my arm across His shoulder. With a smile, He whispered, "Oh, how My Father loves you! Oh, how I love you! There is a day coming when you will see My love for mankind demonstrated from the hilltop and then you will know the depth, the height, the length, the width of My love for you!"

At that precise moment, the sun made its grand appearance over the horizon, casting its golden light on the Master's face; it appeared that Jesus outshined the sun. I stepped aside, slightly trembling.

"Master?"

He turned and looked at me with such piercing eyes that my heart nearly stopped.

*There is so much more to this Man than I know. He is completely and totally different from anyone I have ever met.*

"Yes, Peter?" Jesus responded.

"It looked like You were...that You were shining."

"I am the light of the world," He replied.

The sleeping disciples stirred and Jesus announced, "It is time to greet the day, My friends."

Quickly rising, they joined the Master and me for a hearty breakfast. The Master then led us to a nearby town. In a very short time a large crowd gathered. Jesus hurried through the busy streets, stopping only once to speak to a woman who was clearly a prostitute.

Once we arrived at the west gate, the Master came to an abrupt halt. I looked for the reason but saw nothing.

*Jesus is staring at—a tree?*

I stepped closer and saw that the object of His attention was actually hiding behind a myrtle tree. Upon a closer inspection, I realized that the man had leprosy. I shuddered with disgust and instinctively stepped back, for there was no disease as repulsive as leprosy.

Jesus walked toward him, and the leper remained silent and unmoving. As Jesus stood before him, the man jumped to his feet. The crowd quickly scattered and, I must confess that I, too, hurried away, as did all of the other disciples. Jesus alone remained. The leper stood face to face with the Master.

I was highly offended by the leper's boldness. Lepers were forbidden by our Law to fellowship with others. If someone should accidently come near them, the lepers were commanded to shout, 'Unclean! unclean!' so that everyone would clearly know their polluted condition. They were also commanded to tear their clothing, shave their heads and cover the bottom half of their faces with cloth, which this man had done.

Every Jewish person believed that leprosy came directly from God. That was why physicians would not even attempt to cure it. Instead, lepers were placed under the care of the priests who waited to see what God would do, for only God could cleanse leprosy. Once a person became leprous, he was considered dead even though it might take years for him to physically die.

Suddenly, the leper fell to his knees. Jesus looked on with great compassion as He knelt beside him. The leper slowly looked up; the filthy rag covering his face fell off. I was horrified to see that one of his ears and much of his nose and mouth had been eaten away by the leprosy. His appearance was disgusting. He was the most repulsive human I had ever seen. Even from where I stood, I could smell him, and it was absolutely revolting!

Jesus extended His hand to this grossly disfigured man, which the leper accepted. Jesus helped him to his feet. As they stood face to sickening face, the leper pleaded, "Lord, I am horribly afflicted in both body and soul. I know that You can do anything; I know that You can make me clean, if You are willing."

*Who does this man think he is? He has no right to speak to the Master much less touch Him—the Law forbids it!*

Tears trailed down his cheeks as Jesus laid His hand on the sides of his face. With great compassion He said, "I am willing. Be clean!"

Immediately, the man's ear, nose and mouth grew back as well as his fingers and toes. His skin instantly became like that of a baby, smooth and clear.

Only God could cleanse a leper, and Jesus just cleansed this man—I saw it with my own eyes as did the crowd around me!

The cleansed man started laughing and crying at the same time. He threw himself into Jesus' arms and both fell backwards onto the ground, laughing hilariously. I was too stunned to do anything but stare.

Having thoroughly exhausted themselves they lay face up on the ground. Jesus propped himself up on His elbow and said, "Tell no man what has been done for you until you have shown yourself to the priest and he has pronounced you clean. Then offer the gift Moses commanded as a testimony so that you will have legal proof that you are now thoroughly cleansed and then you can effectively testify."[33]

After thanking Him the man scrambled to his feet and said, "Thank You! Thank You for cleansing me!"

With a leap, he ran off headed for the temple in Jerusalem. The crowds responded by flocking around Jesus, entreating Him to heal their infirmities.

We were well aware that the Pharisees had sent their "spies" to follow the Master and send reports back to Jerusalem. I could not help but chuckle as I realized what Jesus just did—He just sent them a firsthand report of His activities in the person of that cleansed leper!

*This is going to cause quite an uproar among the religious leaders in Jerusalem. They definitely won't like this.*

Jesus turned and said to us, "From this point on I can no longer enter a town openly. Come, let us leave the city."

We walked until dark. As the multitude made camp in an open

field, we followed Jesus to a more secluded place. My wife, Miriam, and the other women set about preparing food while we built a fire.

I could not stop thinking about the leper. Not only had the leper broken the Law, but so did Jesus in responding to him. Curious I said, "Master, that leper broke the Law when he approached You."

"Simon Peter, I desire mercy not sacrifice."

"But the Law—."

"My dear friend, take your eyes off the Law and take a good look at that leper," He said as He threw another stick on the fire.

"Peter, that man not only had to bear the physical pain of his disease, but every day he felt the pain of being completely rejected and shunned by his own people, his family, his friends, by those who should love him the most. Every single day, he was painfully alone and without any hope.

"Peter, I did not come to condemn the lost, but to forgive, to love and redeem them.

"Being My disciple is not about following a set of rules and regulations. Have I not broken some of your traditions, which the Pharisees derived from the Law? I expose what is false. Simon, never stone anyone for religion's sake.

"Your leaders see the person steeped in sin and, for the sake of the Law, shout, 'Crucify him that the Law might be fulfilled!' But I see the person steeped in sin and reach out with compassion and mercy inviting him to follow Me. Do not think that I came to abolish the Law and the Prophets; I did not come to abolish, but to fulfill.[34]

"Peter, being My disciple is based on love; it is primarily about loving God and loving others. To many of the Pharisees religion is about traditions and rituals. Many of them believe and teach that a person's ability to keep the Law and all of the traditions determines their standing before God, and that is simply not true. And because they use this as their standard to judge, they are convinced that I am a man who is serving Satan. This places them in a dangerous position because they are unable to even consider that I am the One sent from God."

I responded, "Until you came along I had never seen a religion that cared more for the person than it did for its form."

"Peter, when I saw that leper crouched behind that tree like some kind of forsaken animal, I was moved with compassion, not judgment. I was fully aware of the rulings made by the Pharisees and Scribes concerning his uncleanness, but his suffering mattered more to Me than some ruling of man.

"I came to bring hope to the hopeless, to bring life to those who are dead, to love those who are unloved. I came to redeem mankind that all men might enter into an intimate relationship with God, the very thing that was in My Father's heart upon creation."

"I have so much to learn, Master."

"And I have so much to give, Peter."

Tired and with much to think about, I bid everyone good-night and retired to my pallet.

Miriam fell asleep immediately, but I laid for what seemed like hours watching the stars and wondering how I would ever be like the Master. It is the duty of a disciple to become like his Teacher, but this One seemed so perfect that I felt as though I would never even be remotely like Him.

I was still awake when the Master rose. He quietly walked a short distance away and then fell to the ground pulling His prayer shawl over His head. I watched until sleep overtook me.

The following morning, Jesus announced that we were returning to Capernaum.

The news of the leper's cleansing spread like wildfire. The Master's fame went from that of a single candle to a glorious bonfire overnight. People came to hear Him, not only from Galilee and the country around, but from Jerusalem and Judea, which lay a great way off; for news about Him had spread all over Syria.

With Capernaum in sight, my wife took my hand and whispered, "It is good to be home."

Her dark eyes danced.

The people of Capernaum were excited to see that the Master had returned. Word spread quickly that the Rabbi was back. With so many people following Him, Jesus took the shortest route through the city even though it was the most crowded.

Coming upon a group of elderly men gathered around a well, Jesus stopped and listened to their debate. They were speaking about matters pertaining to the Law. To my delight, Jesus took a seat among them. Since we were not rabbis, the disciples and I stood behind the Master. The crowd gathered around as well.

Obviously pleased with their growing audience, their discussions escalated.

"It has been believed for generations that a sick person cannot be healed until all his sins have been forgiven!" one of them argued.

"I know that is what our fathers believed, but look at Job, he neither sinned nor condoned sin," another decreed.

"Where you find suffering, you will find that there is sin, and that is a fact!" one of the youngest among them shouted.

*Why is Jesus remaining silent? He is a greater Teacher than all of these men put together. Surely He has an answer for them.*

"We have all been taught that a sick person is someone with whom God is angry!" another added.

At this point, the Master stood. Taking a step forward, He cleared His throat. The debate came to an abrupt halt as every eye looked at this gentle Man dressed in the common attire of a mere laborer. Surrounded by white haired men dressed in finery, Jesus appeared much younger than His thirty years.

*What is He going to do?*

Without saying a word, He walked over to one of the men who had been silent throughout the debate. The man embraced a pair of crutches. Protruding from underneath the edge of his outer garment was a deformed foot.

The Master smiled and asked, "What is your name, My friend?"

Straightening his shoulders, he answered, "I am Matthias, the son of Tyrus."

Laying His hand on the man's shoulder, Jesus said, "Do not be afraid, Matthias, for I have come to seek and save the lost. Rise up and walk, My friend!"

*He healed him! The Master has healed this man!*

Without taking his eyes off of Jesus, the man slowly stood. Jesus reached out and took his crutches. The man took a step then another and another. He exclaimed, "I can walk! Look at me everybody; I can walk!"

The man rejoiced and the crowd exploded in applause. He turned to the Master and said, "Praise the Lord! Oh give thanks to the Lord, for He is good; for His lovingkindness is everlasting!"[35]

Jesus joined him and exclaimed, "Who in the heavens is comparable to the Lord? Who among the sons of the mighty is like the Lord? For He is a God greatly feared in the council of the holy ones and awesome above all those who are around Him! O Lord God of hosts, who is like You? O mighty Lord, Your faithfulness also surrounds You. You rule the swelling of the sea; when its waves rise, You tell them to be still! O Lord God of hosts, who is like You?"[36]

At this point, the healed man ran off. The sick pushed their way through the awestruck crowd to Jesus, and He healed them all. Jesus then stepped up on a large rock and addressed the crowd saying, "You search the Scriptures because in them you think you have eternal life."

His words fell like a raindrop on the petal of a rose.

"But," He continued, "it is the Scriptures that testify of Me."[39]

With a nod, He stepped down motioning for us to follow. The elders barely noticed His departure, for they had already begun another debate.

Andrew and I tried to clear a path before the Master, but found it quite difficult. Turning to the Master, trying to be heard over the noise of the crowd, I shouted, "What shall we do? The crowd is too great!"

Jesus answered, "Let us retire to your house."

We turned around and pushed our way through.

Upon arriving home, we discovered that my wife and mother-in-law had sent word to our friends and relatives that the Master was in the house. Many came to dine with us. As we reclined around the table, it was with great delight and a significant amount of pride that I related the many miracles and great exploits I had seen Jesus do on our journeys throughout Galilee. The Master added many commentaries on the various events, which further endeared Him to my friends and family.

Overnight, word had spread throughout the entire district that the Master was back. Early the next morning, a knock on our door brought me to my feet. The servant of a well-known man in the city handed us an invitation to come to his house. Jesus responded, "We will go."

The servant responded with great delight and then hurried off to share the good news with his master.

When the time came, the servant reappeared and led us through the dusty streets. I wondered what new adventure awaited us, for every day with the Master was a new day, never boring, always exciting and filled with many wonders. Turning to Andrew, I jokingly said, "So, what do you think? Should we leave this boring life and go fishing."

Shoving me, he answered, "One day with the Master is better than ten thousand days fishing."

"Just thought I'd check," I answered.

We turned the corner and saw a very large group of people gathered in the yard of a certain house. "This must be the place," I said to no one in particular.

The house was so full that children were sitting in the windows.

The servant indicated that this was indeed the home of his master. Stepping forward, I took it upon myself to clear a path through the crowd for Jesus. With much effort, we finally made it to the front door. Peering into the covered gallery that ran round the courtyard and opened into the various rooms, I saw a man standing on a table, waving his arms wildly. Seeing us, he shouted, "Forgive me that I cannot properly greet you. As you can see my humble home is filled to capacity, for many want to hear the words of the Rabbi."

Seeing Jesus, the people stepped aside to make room for us to enter. Inviting Jesus to join him on the table, the man greeted Him with a kiss saying, "Rabbi, share with us the words of eternal life."

He then stepped down. Jesus began to teach. I managed to squeeze in a little closer as did John and James. Not too far away sat a group of Scribes and Pharisees with their arms folded tightly across their chest and their eyes glaring.

Ignoring them, I listened with fascination as Jesus expounded on the Law and the Prophets.

*Where does He get this incredible knowledge? He is a carpenter's son, not the son of a rabbi nor the son of an educated man, and yet He speaks with great wisdom and amazing understanding!*

The man sitting to my right complained under his breath. He was saying that it was not proper for a man to preach in a house on a weekday. Before I could respond, the man sitting beside him answered, "That may be, but I have never heard a message so full of life nor seen a man so tender and kind as He."

I nodded in full agreement as did several others.

Suddenly, a shower of dust rained down on me. Looking up, I saw a beam of light streaming through a small opening. Every eye in the place was now turned upward. As the hole grew larger, I was surprised to see four men working fervently to remove the tiles. The Master watched closely. It never occurred to me to stop them; I was much too curious as to their mission to think of such a thing.

Once the opening had grown to a considerable size, the men quickly removed the framework that held the tiles. They then disappeared only to return carrying a pallet on which they had tied ropes on the four corners. With great care, they lowered the pallet through the opening. The people quickly moved out of its way while myself, James, John and Matthew reached up to steady it.

*How will Jesus respond to this intrusion, this interruption, not to mention the destruction of this man's roof?*

I glanced at our host. He seemed happier than a sheep grazing in a green pasture. Jesus stepped down and made His way to the pallet on which laid a paralyzed man. Jesus looked up at the four pleading faces peering down at Him. One of the men cried out saying, "Please Rabbi, would you heal our friend?"

*These men must really love this man to go to such lengths as this!*

The paralyzed man looked at Jesus with fear-filled eyes. I could only imagine the turmoil he must have felt.

No one moved; every eye was riveted on the Master. The room was thick with a mixture of curiosity and expectation.

At this point, Jesus laid His hand on the man's chest and, with great tenderness, said, "Take heart son, your sins have been forgiven."

Words of shock and disbelief swept through the room. I looked at the Scribes and Pharisees; they were clearly outraged.

Jesus turned to face them. Their contempt for Him was obvious. He said, "Why are you debating about these things in your minds? You say to yourself, 'Why does this one speak thus? He blasphemes!'"

*The fire just got kindled.*

"Which is easier to say, 'Your sins are forgiven' or to say, 'Get up, pick up your pallet and walk'?"

*The water is boiling.*

"But, so that you may know that the Son of Man has authority on earth to forgive sins—." He turned His attention back to the paralytic and continued, "I say to you, get up, pick up your pallet and go home."

*The whole thing just blew up!*

Color flooded the paralyzed man's pale face as energizing life poured through his limbs. He slowly lifted, what was just seconds ago, his useless legs and arms. His eyes were filled with, not just tears, but also childlike wonder as he looked at the One who restored not only his hope, but also his life.

The man pushed himself up to a sitting position. Looking at his legs, he swung them over the side of his pallet then slowly stood.

The people squirmed. Their murmuring cut through the silence like the bleating of a sheep in the quiet stillness of the night.

*They are thinking what I am thinking. How can Jesus offer this man forgiveness for his sins? Only God can forgive sins.*

Without saying a word, the man untied the ropes, rolled up his pallet and tucked it under his arm. With a smile on his face, he headed for the front door as the crowd made way for him.

A man shouted out, "I have never seen anything like this! What kind of man is this Jesus of Nazareth that God would grant Him such authority?"

The healed man walked out as the people reached out to touch him as if he was a god. Others followed praising Jehovah for sending a man with such authority to Israel.

I found it interesting that the people expressed their admiration of Jesus, not as the Messiah or the Son of God, but merely as a man to whom God had given great authority.

The Scribes and Pharisees stood discussing amongst themselves what they should do with this One who was quickly growing in popularity.

*Not only is Jesus performing signs and wonders, but He has just demonstrated that He can forgive sins. The Pharisees teach that one must be forgiven to be healed. This man was healed! Therefore, Jesus' claim to forgive sins must be true! The Pharisees have quite a problem on their hands—if Jesus continues to heal people in this manner it would most certainly bring an end to orthodox religion as we know it.*

The Pharisees turned to the crowd and loudly expressed their contempt for Jesus and for what He just did.[38]

*I can see the hatred in their eyes.*

I looked at the Master, who was holding a small child in His arms and speaking with a woman who was probably the child's mother. He seemed unaffected by the response of the Pharisees.

*Jesus just signed His own death warrant—I wonder if He knows it?*

I continued to watch as the Master moved around the room speaking to various people. He laughed easily and embraced all who would allow Him.

Every day brought a deeper revelation of this One who was so much more than a mere man with authority from God. I had seen Jesus heal, but to think that He could also forgive sins was even more than I could digest. After all, I had been taught since a young child that only God could forgive sins.

My experience with religion had only been the black and white letter of the Law, which involved a judgement that was void of mercy. But Jesus demonstrated a whole new dynamic, a whole new dimension to this thing called religion. At the very center of all that Jesus did was perfect love. His heart yearned to love, and He delighted in being loved.

In my journeys with the Master, early on, I came to realize that mercy has a voice as well as sin. I also recognized that the never-ending mercy of God hears our cries and never fails to respond. His responses may not look the way I think they should, neither does He respond according to my time frame, but He surely cares, and He will respond.

# CHAPTER ELEVEN

Laban's hoarse voice cuts through the darkness, "Shhh, Peter! Someone is coming!"

"Father, we place ourselves in Your care and ask for Your protection and help," I quickly pray.

First, I hear the footsteps and then the dreaded sound of the key turning in the lock that never fails to cause me to cringe.

The sound of mocking laughter lets me know that this is not a friend. "What fairy tales are you telling now, Christian?" Brutus asks.

"I am telling the greatest story that ever was or ever will be. The story that never ends—."

"We'll see about that!" he interrupts as he cracks his whip in the air. "You see, Christian, your story will end because you will end. You will cease to exist, and then I will be sad because I won't have you to entertain me."

*Oh, Divine Master, help me love this man, I pray!*

I respond, "You may kill my body, but you cannot touch my soul. And, if you kill me, you will only be delivering me from this world of sin and death and into the arms of Jesus Christ, my beloved Lord and Savior."

Brutus curses and says, "You will be mine! You will surrender!"

He delivers a swift kick to my rib cage. Gasping for breath, I silently pray.

Brutus bends low and grabs my face with his hands, causing me to look at him. Squinting because of the light, I see the angry face of a hurting man.

I say, "My friend, I must tell you that there is One that you should fear and that is the One who can not only kill the body, but can also deliver your soul to hell. You should know that He is not willing that any should perish, but you should also know that He judges rightly. He longs to embrace you, He longs to—."

"Shut up!" he shouts stepping back, "I will not allow you to pollute my mind!"

His whip cuts through the air wrapping itself around my back and midsection. My old, tattered garment offers no protection. I clench my jaw so tightly that a tooth breaks.

As Brutus delivers one blow after another, I throw myself into the arms of my Beloved and silently cry out, "I want to know You, Lord! I want to see Your face! I want to feel Your touch! I want to hear Your voice!"

Exhausted, Brutus finally stops. Leaning against the post he says, "So, Simon Peter, are you ready to become another notch in my belt? Are you ready to deny this man you call the Messiah?"

Gasping for air I reply, "How can I deny truth? How can I deny pure love? How can I deny kindness and beauty and goodness? I cannot. How can I deny the One who endured sufferings much greater than anything I have endured all because of His great love for me? Brutus, you ask me to do something that is impossible. You ask me to deny the One who died for me. How could I ever do such a thing and betray One who is so lovely and perfect and good?"

"Fool!" Brutus says as he snatches the torch from its holder. "You are a stupid fool!"

The door slams shut. I pray for him until I either fall asleep or pass out; I am not sure which.

"Peter, are you okay?"

I hear the voice but cannot respond.

*Perhaps, this is the end, Lord. Perhaps, this is the day that I will be reunited with You. Oh, gracious King, take me home, I pray.*

Darkness sweeps over me like the wind sweeps over the desert.

Searing pain wakes me. I lift my head, and the room spins violently. My entire torso feels as though it is on fire.

I remind myself that this is but a small sample of what the Master endured for me. I have taken only fifteen lashes, but my Lord endured over thirty.

"Peter, are you okay?" Justus asks.

"I still love my Lord, so I am doing well."

"I did not know what to do, so I did what I have heard you do so much—I prayed. But, I don't know if it counted because I don't really know how to pray, and I don't even know if God hears sinners. But, I didn't know what else to do," Justus says obviously quite anxious.

With a grateful heart I reply, "Oh, Justus, that blesses me! Thank you for praying. And as for whether or not God heard you—God came for sinners; He hears every heart that turns to Him."

Justus continues, "I must confess that I was so fearful that I asked Laban to pray too. I thought that if God refused to hear my prayer, then He might hear him since he has killed only one man compared to my three."

Laban jumped in saying, "I didn't know what to do either, so I just talked to God just like I am talking to you. I sure hope He didn't mind."

"Justus, God does not look at your righteousness or lack thereof to determine whether or not he hears your prayers. God hears the cry of those who look to Him. Laban, there is no formula for prayer. Prayer is simply man communicating with his Creator," I answer.

"What kind of God hears men like me?" Justus asks his voice fading into the darkness.

"A God that is gracious and compassionate, slow to anger, abounding in lovingkindness and relenting of evil," I answer trying desperately to block out the excruciating pain in my body.[39]

"Your God is unlike any god I have ever heard of," Laban responds.

"That is a true statement," I answer.

"I have never known a god or a man to have a character like that," Justus adds.

"That is exactly why, my friends, that you need to experience the redeeming love of Jesus of Nazareth. You must know Him, for in Him alone, is eternal life. You can come to the Father only through the Son."

"I hate to ask, Peter, since you must be in terrible pain, but I am a desperate man with very little time left. You have awakened in me a hunger that must be satisfied, a longing that will not be silenced, a desperation that demands an answer. Are you able, my friend, to continue on? Do you have the strength to finish the story?" Justus asks.

"Nothing would strengthen me more than to speak of the One I love so dearly. But, I must confess I cannot remember where I left off."

Laban is quick to answer, "You just told us about the paralyzed man whose sins were forgiven and who Jesus healed."

"So I did."

Whispering a prayer for supernatural strength, I resume telling the greatest story that has ever been told.

# CHAPTER TWELVE

W e stepped outside the house only to find that the streets were crowded with people who were curious and eager to see this miracle-working Rabbi. I looked over my shoulder at the damaged roof and saw the healed man's friends happily replacing the tiles.

"I do not think I will ever forget this day," I said to Andrew, James and John.

"Nor will I," James responded.

John exclaimed, "Never have I seen such love demonstrated!"

"'Tis a beautiful thing," James remarked.

"I am amazed at how this Rabbi consistently loves— even in the presence of His enemies!" John added.

"It is quite amazing," I said.

The weeks passed and Jesus continually poured Himself out for the sake of the people. Spring arrived quickly.

As we followed Jesus through the city streets, the crowds were so great that we could barely walk. Jesus turned to us and said, "Let us go to the seashore where there is more room."

Like a shepherd leading His sheep out to pasture, the Master slowly made His way through the city streets. The crowd grew in number as we went.

Walking a short distance down the rocky beach, Jesus stopped before a large, flat stone that jutted out over the beach, making it the perfect platform. As graceful as a deer, Jesus climbed up and sat down, which signified that He was about to say something important. The people excitedly gathered around and quickly grew silent.

*It is so good to be here. The bright sun provides just enough warmth from the cool spring air.*

For hours, Jesus taught, and the people eagerly devoured His words. Both men and women, old and young listened closely to the Master and were visibly impacted.

Having concluded, Jesus blessed the people then jumped down. We followed as He left the beach and headed for the custom house. His eyes were fixed on one booth in particular. He had that look in His eyes that usually meant that some adventure was about to happen.

When we were a stone's throw away, I recognized the man sitting at the booth. His name was Matthew. He was a custom house official, a highly specialized tax collector for Galilee under Herod Antipas, which is a little better than being a tax collector for Judea, which is under Roman rule, but not much. Regardless of who he worked for, tax collectors were detestable whether Roman or Galilean. No one liked them, and it was against the Law for us to fellowship with them.

I had seen Matthew, on several occasions, listening as the Master taught by the seashore. Obviously, the Master's messages did nothing to transform this man, for he continued to do what he did best and that was rob the people.

*Jesus is probably going to challenge his dishonest methods of accounting!*

*This could be fun!*

I increased my pace until I was beside Him. The Master stopped just beside Matthew's booth. Without looking up, Matthew grunted saying, "I'll be with you in a moment."

There were two types of tax collectors under Herod's rule. The first type collected ground, income and poll taxes. The second was called a custom house official, which was what Matthew was. This type provided many more opportunities for dishonesty. The custom house officials taxed all imports and exports; everything that was bought and sold—bridge-money, road-money, harbor-dues, town-dues, etc. The custom house officials often invented taxes on such things as axles, wheels, animals, pedestrians, admission to markets, bridges, boats, crossing rivers, on any object known to man. They were often guilty of partiality in that they would extend favor to those they liked while exacting taxes from those whom they disliked.

I looked down at Matthew who was thoroughly absorbed in counting his latest acquisition. Taking out a ledger, he recorded the figures. With one sweep of his hand, Matthew divided the coins placing them in separate leather pouches. The largest pouch remained on the table; the other was hidden inside his garment.

*What kind of man could steal from his own people?*

The fact that Matthew was a custom house official said much about his lack of character, for no self-respecting Jewish man would ever accept such a degrading position.

*This is a profession that is plagued with temptation and most often corrupted. It is extremely rare to find a tax collector who is truly honest. I cannot say that I have ever met one neither have I ever heard of one. Because of this, everyone knows that it is especially difficult for tax gatherers to ever change. I sure do hope the Master exposes this man!*

A hand on my shoulder startled me. I looked into the Master's eyes and saw a depth of love that seemed endless. Leaning close, He whispered, "Simon, I love this man. I desire to see him redeemed, not destroyed."

I merely nodded. With a smile, Jesus turned and laid both of His hands on the table. Matthew looked up obviously expecting a customer; his artificial smile quickly faded away. Jesus looked on with kindness even though it appeared that He was looking into the very depths of Matthew's soul.

Matthew's hand instinctively gripped the leather pouch beneath his garment, which was hidden from the eyes of all but One.

Jesus extended His hand saying, "Matthew, won't you come and follow Me?"

*Just what is the Master doing? I do not want this man to be part of our group! Doesn't He know that he is a thieving tax collector, a traitor to Israel! How can He do this?*

I was just about to protest, when the unthinkable actually happened—Matthew stood to his feet, tears flowed unhindered down his young face and he nodded. Without saying a word, he handed his ledger and money bag to his assistant and then walked away! He walked away from his dreams, from any hope for advancement and from a very promising future.[40]

He took his place by the Master's side who put His arm around his shoulder and pulled him close. I could not hear what Jesus said to him as they walked along, but knowing the Master I was certain that He spoke words of kindness and affirmation.

For the remainder of the day, Matthew stayed by the Master's side like a dog stays close to its owner. I kept my distance from Matthew as did the other disciples, which meant that I could not be by the Master's side, which was my custom.

I was so glad when the sun set and Matthew retired to his own home. We gathered around the campfire. John, being the youngest, took his rightful place at the Master's right hand while I sat at His left.

*I do not understand why the Master invited someone like Matthew to follow Him. This is bordering on treason and makes no sense to me.*

I forced myself to stop thinking about Matthew and focused on having a good time. We told stories and laughed and sang and danced. It may have been an awful day, but it ended well.

The Master was the One who called the night to an end. Making His way around the circle, He blessed each one of us. When He came to my wife, He laid his hand on her head, blessed her and kissed her forehead.

The Master whispered to her, "Behold the handmaiden of the Lord!"

A tear trickled down her cheek.

*I know how she feels. There is something different about the Master's touch, something that touches the very depths of one's being.*

After pausing a moment longer, He then moved on to His mother, Mary, and blessed her.

Miriam laid her head against my shoulder and quietly wept. The Master kissed His mother and escorted her to her pallet. He bid her good-night and then walked a short distance away where He knelt in prayer.

I led Miriam to a place not far from the comfort of the campfire. It was there that we spread our pallets. Knowing me so well, my wife waited until I was settled. She then said, "Simon, you have not been yourself this day. What troubles you?"

Rolling over to face her, I answered, "Do you not know? Have you not heard that the Master invited a tax collector to be one of His followers, to be one of us! I do not understand how He could do so!"

"Shhhh, Simon! The others will hear you!" Miriam whispered.

Lowering my voice, I continued, "Miriam, Matthew has, on several occasions, falsely charged me taxes and just think how many times we have been robbed by men just like him! I guarantee you that Matthew lives in a magnificent house with a multitude of servants and eats the food of kings. It is people like you and me that finance his extravagant lifestyle, Miriam!"

"Simon, I do not understand many of the things the Master does or says, but I do know that there has never been anyone like Him in Israel. There is something about Him that is inherently good and causes my heart to want to be like Him. He is unlike the other rabbis. There is something about Him that not only convicts me, but also draws me. His very appearance is gentle and kind, not harsh or self-righteous. Simon, I trust Him even though I do not understand Him. And, this is one of those times when you may have to trust Him without understanding why He would choose someone like Matthew."

I made no comment but simply turned away.

"Simon," she said laying her delicate hand on my shoulder, "From the first time we began following the Master, we have seen Him pursue and choose weak, unqualified, sinful men, women and children to be His followers and closest friends. Matthew is simply another one of those; he just happens to be a tax collector.

"Simon, have you stopped to think that you and I are no different. We were, and still are, weak, broken, immature, sinful people and yet the Master chose us, didn't He?"

I listened to the wisdom of my wife and fought back the tears. I knew she was right, but my heart resisted. I did not know at the time that I was filled with self-righteous pride and jealousy, which blind the heart and dull the mind.

"I know that you are right, Miriam, but I cannot accept this man as one of us."

Kissing the back of my head, she bid me good-night, leaving me to wrestle with my soul.

Staring at the star-filled sky, I asked the God of heaven to change my heart.

At first light, I woke with a stiff neck. Sitting up, I saw that Matthew had already arrived and was deep in conversation with the Master.

*This is going to be another long day.*

Two very long days passed, and Matthew continued to follow Jesus like a puppy nipping at his master's heels, eager for his attention. I kept my distance, for I had no desire to be close to Matthew. My heart was turning to stone.

On the third morning, as we sat eating bread and cheese, Matthew, followed by several of his servants, came running into our camp. Tearing a piece of bread, I looked closely at this man. He was wearing a seamless, outer garment made of fine linen. His inner robe was made of purple silk as was his turban.

*Only a very wealthy man could afford clothing like that. He must be a really good thief to have acquired such wealth at such a young age; he could not be more than twenty years of age.*

Matthew quickly approached the Master saying, "I would like to prepare a feast in Your honor. Would You give me the privilege of hosting You and Your disciples this evening?"

Jesus responded, "Matthew, we would be delighted to be your guests."

*This is just great! It's not enough that we have to endure his presence during the day, but now we have to eat in the home of this sinner!*

A very excited Matthew hurried off; his servants followed close behind. I walked away. Miriam joined me saying, "Simon, be careful that you do not allow your heart to become filled with bitterness."

"I know, Miriam. I am trying, but you obviously do not understand."

Taking my hand in hers, she responded, "Come, let us follow the Master, for in doing so you will surely overcome the things that hinder you from being like the Master. But, if you walk away, you will give Satan a place in your life and he will surely devour you."

Smiling at my petite wife, I allowed her to lead me back to the Master who appeared to be waiting for me. Throwing His arm around my shoulder, we set out for a nearby village where the Master taught and healed the sick.

The afternoon sun began its westward descent as we made our way to Matthew's house. Along the way, Jesus talked with us concerning the Kingdom that was soon to come. I found myself unclear as to His message because His words were cloaked in mystery.

Matthew's house sat on the crest of a hill overlooking Capernaum. It was larger and more extravagant than I imagined, which only served to fuel the angry, jealous flame that burned within my heart.

A very excited Matthew, along with nearly a dozen servants, waited for us at the gate. Matthew greeted each of us with a kiss until he came to the Master. At which point, he embraced Him with both arms and kissed His cheeks several times. Jesus responded accordingly and just as warmly.

Matthew then stepped back, threw his arms open wide and exclaimed, "Welcome! You are all welcome! Come, for the table is ready, and my guests await your arrival!"

He ushered us into the courtyard where we were immediately met by a different group of servants who washed our feet, rubbed fragrant oil over them and even washed our sandals.

*Matthew certainly has trained his servants well.*

After they finished, we stepped inside the entrance hall,

which was larger than my entire house. Everywhere I looked were elaborate decorations and lavish furniture. I was growing exceedingly uncomfortable knowing that all of this was possible because of Matthew's occupation. I thought about the tax collectors' common practices of oppressing, exacting, taking bribes and accusing falsely those from whom taxes are due, namely men like me and my anger flared.

*I cannot be part of this!*

I turned around to leave but found myself face to face with John who immediately put his arm on my shoulder and whispered, "Peter, I know how you feel, but just wait. Let us see how the Master responds."

Andrew quickly joined us; my brother's eyes spoke volumes.

"It looks like I'm outnumbered," I replied.

"It certainly looks that way to me," my brother answered. "Come with us, Simon Peter."

I decided to stay even though everything in me wanted to either run away or tell Matthew just what he could do with his money, his house and his expensive furnishings.

With John on one side and Andrew on the other, they escorted me to a bench where we waited for the Master. Matthew came bouncing into the room closely followed by two servants.

*I bet they even follow him to the chamber pot.*

Jesus walked in. Matthew was immediately at His side and escorted Him to the dining hall. I reluctantly followed.

Crossing the threshold, I came to an abrupt halt. Never had I seen such opulence or extravagance. The room was huge. Lavish curtains covered the windows. The amazingly long table was set with gold serving dishes, plates and goblets. About thirty people reclined around the table on silk pillows. I recognized several as tax collectors who were well-known for their blatant, sinful lifestyles.

*It is unlawful for Jewish men to eat with tax collectors and sinners.*

I took a step back and bumped into John; Andrew and James were behind him.

*I'm not the only one uncomfortable.*

Every Jewish child is taught from a very young age that it is against the Law to fellowship with sinners, which includes prostitutes, thieves and others of low reputations such as tax collectors. We all understood that there were many sins that the religious establishment winked at, but to eat with these men, who I knew to be actively involved in blatant sin, was unthinkable.

Not only were we forbidden to eat with sinners, but our custom was to only eat with people who we desired to enter into a close personal relationship with.

*Why would I want to be close friends with sinners? That would ruin my reputation.*

Matthew was introducing Jesus to a man I knew to be one of the most crooked businessmen in Capernaum; he has even stolen from widows and children.

Jesus embraced the man; our eyes met. I saw such compassion, such love in Jesus' eyes that I had to look away, for I knew what filled my eyes.

*Jesus truly loves this man! How is that possible?*

Trembling, I looked at John who seemed just as upset as I.

Jesus moved from person to person, greeting each one as though he was the most important person on the earth. And all the while, a very proud and excited Matthew never left His side.

After greeting all the guests, Jesus took His place as the guest of honor. Matthew then invited us to take our places at the table, which was the last thing I wanted to do. John was the first to move forward. Reluctantly, I followed, taking the place indicated by the servant. The man on my right proudly introduced himself as a tax collector.

*Oh, great! This is just great!*

The room was buzzing with excitement. Servants hurried here and there, placing large platters of rich, luxurious food before us. New guests arrived and Matthew quickly brought them to Jesus who graciously greeted them.

*It is one thing to embrace Matthew who has left his dishonest occupation, but to embrace unconverted, unrepentant sinners is another thing altogether.*

I could not believe my eyes when several Pharisees and Scribes entered the dining hall. They made their way across the great room and leaned against the wall just behind James, John, Nathaniel, Andrew, Philip and myself.

*What are they doing here? They think it scandalous to be seen in the company of tax collectors. They teach that anyone of any reputation should separate himself from the likes of men like these.*

To the strict orthodox Jews, there is a clear distinction between the people who keep the Law and the common masses who do not observe all the rules and regulations of the Pharisees. The orthodox Jews are forbidden to have anything to do with those who do not keep the letter of the Law. They must have no fellowship with them at all, must not talk with them nor go on a journey with them. As much as possible, they must not do business with them. And, above all, they must not accept hospitality from or extend hospitality to them.

*The only reason they would subject themselves to the humiliation of being in the presence of sinners, especially tax collectors, is if there is something they want. And what they want is information that they could use to accuse the Master. They have come to spy on Him.*

They were in the room a short time when one of them tapped me on the shoulder. I braced myself knowing that he was not going to ask me to pass the bread.

In a voice loud enough to be heard throughout the room, he asked, "Why does your Teacher eat with tax collectors and sinners?"

I did not know what to say or how to respond. The gauntlet had been cast, and I knew not how to answer.

Many of the Pharisees and Scribes were very careful to maintain a form of godliness, but in pursuing that, they had become even greater enemies to the power of it. These pious men were dressed in the finest of apparel and wore phylacteries on their foreheads and over their hearts. The phylacteries contained a small strip of parchment with portions of the Law written on it. Their purpose was to remind the wearer of the duty of keeping God's commandments both in the head and in the heart.

*Somehow, I think they have forgotten the part about the heart. They know the Law, but do they know the Author of the Law? Do I?*

I looked into the Pharisee's eyes, eyes filled with arrogance and even anger, and I saw my own reflection. I saw myself and conviction flooded my being. I walked into this house with the same self-righteous attitude as these Pharisees. I was no different from them. I have lived in the same manner my entire life. For the first time, I could clearly see the arrogance and jealousy that filled my heart. I saw that I, too, was a man who was very strict about avoiding sinners but not in avoiding sin. I cared more about what people thought about me than I did about doing what was right.

I looked back at Jesus. He was dressed in the garments of a common man. He had no phylactery, no jewels and no extravagant tunic, but He had something so much more valuable—He had a tender, merciful and compassionate heart. He was not concerned about His outward appearance or what others thought of Him. His concern was the inward condition of the heart.

To my surprise, Jesus directed His attention to the Pharisees. Leaning forward He said, "It is not those who are healthy who need a physician, but those who are sick.

"You think that the tax collectors are to be hated and rejected, but they should be embraced with love and compassion because they are sick and in need of a doctor. I am a Physician; therefore, I frequent the company of those who are sick, those who are lost in their sins. Where else, but among those most grievously afflicted, would a physician be found?"

He paused. His words pierced my heart and probably the hearts of many in the room. Standing, He continued, "These men and women are sinners and need a Savior. You think that righteousness should keep Me from them, but I have not come to call the righteous, but the sinners to repentance. It is to a sinful world that I am sent; therefore, My duty lies most with those who are the greatest sinners in it."

The Master sat back down then continued, "So, go and study the Law and learn what this means: 'I desire compassion and not animal sacrifice.' I did not come to call the righteous, but sinners."[41]

It was so quiet in that room that you could hear a needle drop. I looked at John who had tears in his eyes.

*He is so tenderhearted.*

The Master's words were like unexpected guests—no one knew they were coming and, once they arrived, we were not sure what to do with them.

The Scribes and Pharisees appeared furious. Thumbing their noses at Him, they stormed out of the room without saying a word.

We continued our meal, but I could hardly eat because I was filled with so much conviction. The Master's word had pierced my soul. His words insinuated that while the Pharisees were very religious they were also full of pride, prejudice, harshness and hatred. His words meant death to Jewish pride and elitism. It was clear that it was not enough to be acquainted with the letter of the Law, but one must also understand the meaning, the heart of it, and live according to compassion and mercy. What a concept! A concept that I had never considered before!

Matthew's guests started leaving. I took my place with the other disciples in the courtyard while Matthew and Jesus bid the guests farewell.

"Can you believe what the Master said to those Pharisees?" Nathaniel asked.

"He wasn't just talking to the Pharisees and Scribes, He was talking to me," John answered.

"And to me," I added.

"I am just as guilty as the rest of you," Andrew added.

Judas mumbled something that I could not understand.

"What did you say?" I asked.

"Nothing, I said nothing," he replied.

Just then Matthew and the Master, followed by several servants, joined us. A very happy Matthew said "Come, I have prepared a place for you to stay the night."

With a heavy heart, I followed Matthew to a very large room where numerous pallets awaited us. Relieved that the day was over, I collapsed onto a very thick pallet exhausted more from the battle that had been going on in my heart than from any activity I had done.

Jesus bid us good-night and then followed Matthew out.

It was only a matter of minutes before the others were snoring. After tossing and turning for quite some time, I decided to go for a walk. Making as little noise as possible, I tiptoed across the squeaky floor.

Walking through Matthew's beautiful garden, my heart grew heavier and heavier.

*I cannot endure the agony, the pain of my sin any longer.*

I began searching for the One I had come to love so deeply. Leaving the garden, I found Him in the pasture, sitting among the lilies, lost in prayer.

I watched in amazement at this Man who so diligently and lovingly attends to the needs of others throughout the day and then gives Himself to prayer during much of the night.

*What kind of fire burns within this Man that He so selflessly and sacrificially gives Himself to the heart of God and to the heart of man?*

His shoulders shake as His prayers are watered by His tears.

*What or who does He pray for that moves His heart so? I do not believe that I have ever shed a tear in prayer.*

Looking heavenward, I pray, "Father, I have sinned against You and against Matthew. Please forgive me. I do not know how to change myself; I need Your help."

Not knowing what else to say, having never really prayed like that before, I stopped.

"Peter, come and join Me," the Master called out.

"I do not want to disturb You," I answered.

"You are always welcome to come into My presence, Peter."

I was in turmoil, desiring to be with the Master, but also feeling the crippling shame over my jealous, self-righteous attitude towards Matthew.

"Perhaps You'd rather be alone."

"Peter, have you forgotten how much I enjoy you, how much I love you? Have you forgotten that I delight in watching you grow and change and mature? I do not wait for you to become perfect so that I can enjoy you, My friend. No, I love and enjoy you even in your weakness. Peter, I understand you much more than you understand yourself, and I do not condemn you, neither do I accuse you—that is what Satan does. My love convicts you while inviting you to come closer, to draw nearer, for in My presence you are changed.

"I can see that you have doubts, My friend. Let us look at your relationship with your brother, Andrew. You love your brother, do you not?"

"Of course I do. I would die for him!"

"Is he perfect?"

"Not even close," I answered.

"Do you enjoy him even though he has faults?"

"Very much."

"If you are able to love and enjoy your brother just like he is, what makes you think that I am not able to love you in the same way?"

He paused then continued, "The truth is, Peter, that I love to a degree that you cannot even fathom. My love and delight over you is greater than anything you could ever imagine. Now come and tell Me what has been troubling you."

I sat down a short distance away, took a deep breath and began, "So much has happened today. Many of my beliefs have been challenged. Such as—." I looked away unable to continue because of the fear of exposing the darkness within my soul, which I was certain would lead to punishment, or even worse, rejection.

"Never be afraid to tell Me what is on your heart, for I am a good Shepherd who loves His sheep even when they are weak and stray off the beaten path. Peter, your weaknesses do not surprise Me. Neither will they ever cause Me to turn you away."

Taking a deep breath, I answered, "Well, I am not accustomed to eating with—."

"Yes?"

"With sinners and tax collectors!" I blurted out.

"Is there more?" He asked.

"I have been angry, jealous and clearly arrogant in my actions and in my heart since You invited Matthew to be one of Your disciples," I confessed while inwardly bracing myself for what I was sure would be some form of displeasure and rejection.

Jesus responded, "Peter, I fellowship with sinners that I might see them restored. Is it not natural for a shepherd to seek his lost sheep? Of course it is. And it is also only natural, upon finding that sheep, to have more joy over it than over a multitude of sheep that are safe in the pen. To not go after a lost sheep would be completely foreign to the thinking of a good shepherd.

"Peter, I have come to seek and save the lost, to show them that My Father is abounding in lovingkindness and that He longs to walk and talk with His children just as He did with Adam in the garden of Eden."

"I have much to learn, Master. I have been so angry at You and so arrogant towards Matthew," I replied.

"I know," He answered.

"You knew? I thought I hid it from You. You never acted like You knew. Not once did You treat me any differently," I replied quite shocked.

Jesus answered, "Simon, I did not come to condemn, but to save. Love transforms; condemnation destroys. It is the lovingkindness of God that leads men to repentance, My friend."

"I am truly sorry," I said.

"Peter, there are two fundamental differences between My message and the teachings of the Scribes and Pharisees. The first is that I offer forgiveness of sins, and the second is that I embrace sinners. They choose not to do either. The truth is, Peter, that when you have done all you can do, you are still an unprofitable servant, for your righteousness is as filthy rags before My Father. According to your rabbis, righteousness comes by the Law, but the Law only brings death. It is the Spirit that gives life, My friend."

We talked until I could stay awake no longer. With a renewed heart, I bid Him good-night and retired to my room where I quickly fell asleep. I dreamed that I was invited to a wedding banquet where many of the guests were Gentiles, tax collectors and sinners. As I watched, both Jews and Gentiles joined hands and became one bride who was beautiful and dressed in the finest linen. I could not believe my eyes! A blast from a ram's horn summoned the Bridegroom. I turned to see

Jesus sitting on a glorious throne. A voice announced, "Let us rejoice and be glad and give the glory to Him, for the marriage of the Lamb has come and His bride has made herself ready."

Jesus stood; He was dressed in white. His eyes were a flame of fire and upon His head were many crowns. He turned and, upon seeing His bride, smiled a thousand smiles. A robe was placed upon Him that was dipped in blood. His voice, like the sound of many waters, filled the room saying, "For the joy set before Me, I endured the cross! My joy is now complete, for you are My bride, you are My joy!"

Another voice shouted, "His name is the Word of God! His name is the Word of God!"[42]

I woke with a start. I was completely drenched in sweat. Trembling, I quietly slipped out for a breath of fresh air. Climbing the stairs to the roof, I reflected on the dream. I could still hear the voice echoing in my head saying, "His name is the Word of God!"

I lay stretched out underneath the dancing stars pondering my dream. Did it mean anything? And if so, whatever could it mean?

At some point, I fell asleep. I was wakened by a servant who announced breakfast. Joining the others, a new joy filled my heart. I felt clean and no longer burdened down with my sin. It felt so good to no longer sit in judgment against Matthew.

We enjoyed a breakfast that was just as extravagant as our evening meal. Many of the guests from the night before were present. I was struck by their happy countenance; many looked much younger and definitely much more peaceful than they did last night.

The conversation was filled with much laughter as we all shared various humorous adventures. Jesus easily joined in with the light and friendly dialogue, sharing stories of His own. I closely observed His ways, for I longed to be like Him. I was learning and experiencing the reality that the Master enjoyed all kinds of people and found great joy in just being with us.

Having completed our meal, Jesus thanked Matthew for his hospitality and then spoke a blessing over his house. Matthew assured Jesus that He was welcome in his home anytime.

Jesus responded, "Come with Me, Matthew."

"What?" Matthew asked obviously shocked.

"Come and follow Me." With a nod, Jesus left; we followed closely behind. I looked over my shoulder at a speechless Matthew who stood motionless in the doorway. I stopped long enough to motion for Matthew to follow.

*I wonder if he will come.*

Catching up with the Master, we were quickly surrounded by a desperate crowd. Several men pushed their way to the Master and said, "We are disciples of John the Baptizer and have a question for you, Rabbi."

Jesus turned to face them as they continued, "Why is it that we and the Pharisees fast, but Your disciples do not?"

Jesus smiled as He laid His hand on the shoulder of the one closest and answered, "Allow Me ask you a question. Is it right for the guests of the Bridegroom to mourn while He is with them? Is it not a common practice to rejoice during the marriage celebration? Is not all melancholy and sorrow looked upon as being improper and absurd during a wedding celebration?"

"Well, yes, that is true, but what does that have to do with Your disciples not fasting?" the man answered.

Jesus replied, "I am the Bridegroom, just as John taught. And these disciples of Mine are My guests. They cannot mourn while I am with them; it would be inappropriate. But the days *will* come when they will fast because I will not always be with them. In that dark hour, it will be natural and seasonable for them to fast."

*My dream! He's talking about my dream! Is He trying to tell us that He is going to get married? That can't be it because He's not even betrothed, and everyone knows that there can't be a wedding without a betrothal first.*

Jesus reached out and lifted the sleeve of my well-worn outer garment and said, "To have them engage in frequent fasting while they are still young and immature would be like sewing new, unshrunk cloth to that which is worn thin and threadbare. It would be like putting new wine into an old wineskin—the skin would surely burst under the fermenting force of the new wine, and the wine would be spilled and lost."[43]

John's disciples, looking somewhat perplexed, walked away. To my delight, standing just behind the Master, grinning from ear to ear, was Matthew.

*He decided to come!*

I hurried to Matthew's side and put my arm around his shoulder saying, "Never have I seen a happier man than you. Welcome to our family."

"Thank you, Peter," he answered, "I never dreamed that someone like Jesus would even talk to me, much less choose me to be one of His disciples! I still find it difficult to believe. That is why I invited all my tax collector friends to dine at my house with this Rabbi who goes out of His way to embrace worthless men such as I."

My heart was glad for Matthew and my heart was glad for me.

The crowd pressed harder to get as close to Jesus as they possibly could while He spoke to them of a higher way, a greater love, a richer life. At the close of the day, Jesus informed us that it was time to leave Capernaum.

Following the Master down the dusty road, Miriam asked, "Simon, where are we going?"

"I do not know, but I will ask."

I hurried ahead and asked, "Master, what is our destination?"

"Jerusalem, for the feast of the Jews is near," He answered.

After only two days, while we were still far from Jerusalem, we were joined by a flood of travelers headed to the feast. Jesus joyfully and eagerly interacted with old and young, men and women. He went out of His way to extend kindness to the least of them and to teach the truths of the Kingdom to those who would listen.

With each passing day, I grew more and more fascinated with this most unusual Man. He truly was a mystery and a rarity among rabbis.

We finally climbed the last hill, and what a sight it was! People, from all directions, were flocking to the great city like ants rushing to an anthill.

From this vantage point, Jerusalem looked so beautiful; she was spread out like an eagle in flight. Pride filled my heart.

*Oh, how wonderful it is to be Jewish!*

Jesus stopped; His face reflected an ever changing swirl of emotions.

I looked at the afternoon sun, which was beginning to sink low in the sky.

*We must hurry for it will soon be the Sabbath Passover.*

Jesus groaned.

*For what reason?*

Without saying a word, He started out again.

It was now April, the year A.D. 31, and Jerusalem was swarming with thousands of people who had come from far and near. The streets were so crowded with both buyers and sellers that one could barely walk. Lining both sides of the street were booths filled with clothing, jewelry, exotic ointments, spices, herbs, wheat, fish and wine. Numerous sheep, goats, pigeons, donkeys and doves added to the chaos. Beggars stationed themselves strategically near the bustling gates and along street corners hoping to find generous pilgrims.

Passover was certainly a time like none other. With great effort, we finally made it through the hustle and bustle of the streets and arrived at the house of friends.

We were warmly greeted by a servant who led us to the courtyard where a perfect, unblemished lamb, with legs unbroken, was roasting in a clay oven on a skewer of pomegranate wood.

Since a young child, the sight of the Passover lamb has always intrigued me, and I could hardly take my eyes from it now.

Andrew nudged me; I followed him into the house where the atmosphere was that of a great celebration. Everyone was dressed in white. Musicians played; children ran here and there excited about this very special day.

Much care had been given to preparing the place where we would feast. Floor cushions were laid out, waterpots for washing lined the wall and oil lamps were being filled. Servants, as well as others, rushed from place to place bringing trays of food and flasks of wine.

Our host walked in and, with a joyful shout, welcomed us all. Once everyone took their places around the table, the roasted lamb was brought in. The Master looked on intently while our host smiled proudly. The servants then brought in dishes of various bitter herbs, unleavened bread, raw vegetables and haroset, which is a pasty mixture of nuts, fruit and wine.

We entered into the celebration with the ritual hand-washings and prayers. The master of the house then read portions from David's Psalms. We consumed the lamb, all of it, for we were commanded to waste none of it. We ate the various foods in a particular order, for each item has a symbolic meaning for us.

Then, at the end of the meal, at just the right moment, the host's son asked the ceremonial question, the question that would bring the answer as to why we had gathered. He asked, "Father, why is this night different from all other nights?"

With great delight, the boy's father shared the historical account of God's miraculous dealings with Israel which brought about our deliverance from Egypt.

I loved celebrating Passover, for it was a time when we not only looked back, but we also looked forward to the day when we would be redeemed from all remaining Pharaohs, namely Rome.

The celebration went late into the night, but no one tired of it; it was much too dear to us.

At the close of the celebration, I climbed the stairs to the rooftop where we were to sleep. The Passover lamb flashed into my mind as did this passage from Isaiah: "He was oppressed and He was afflicted, yet He did not open His mouth; like a lamb that is led to slaughter, and like a sheep that is silent before its shearers, so He did not open His mouth."[44]

*I haven't thought of that passage in years. Strange that I would think of it tonight.*

With a full stomach and a hopeful heart, I unrolled my pallet and quickly fell asleep.

Early the following morning, we followed the Master to the temple. We passed the sheep gate and came to the pool of Bethseda where Jesus suddenly stopped. He surveyed the great numbers of diseased, blind, lame and paralyzed men and women who lay suffering under the five colonnades. This pitiful crowd remained here day and night waiting for an angel to come down from heaven and stir the waters, because, at that moment, the first person into the pool was healed.

Jesus fixed His gaze on a man lying near the center of the crowd. He was obviously paralyzed. Jesus made His way through the pitiful mass of humanity. Pointing at the paralyzed man, He said, "Do you see that man?"

I nodded.

"He has been in that condition for thirty-eight years."

*How does He know that?*

The Master quickened His pace.

Jesus knelt down by the man's side. Whether the man was old or whether the disease had prematurely aged him, I could not tell. The man was nothing but skin and bones. He returned the Master's gaze with a lifeless, hopeless stare.

*His affliction has taken from him much more than the use of his limbs. This is a man without hope.*

Jesus asked, "Do you wish to get well?"

The man hoarsely answered, "Sir, I do wish to be well. But, when the water is stirred, I have no man to put me into the pool. While I am dragging myself across the stones, another steps in."

Jesus, in a quiet voice, replied, "Get up, pick up your pallet and walk."

Immediately, the man's expression changed from one of utter disbelief to a look of absolute shock. He looked at his useless legs, which suddenly moved. His mouth fell open as he looked back at the Master. "What has happened?" he asked.

Not waiting for an answer, he jumped to his feet. Jesus was laughing as the man hopped from foot to foot delighted with his new legs. He then quickly picked up his pallet, tucked it under his arm and, with great joy, hurried away.

*Just minutes ago that man was unable to even turn himself, and now he is walking and carrying his pallet. Amazing!*

"Carrying his bed!" I said to myself as the realization hit me that it was the Sabbath. Turning my attention to the Master, I nearly shouted,

"He is carrying his pallet, and it is the Sabbath!"

"Indeed he is," He calmly responded.

*It is unlawful for anyone to carry a burden or do work of any kind on the Sabbath. This man will be noticed by everyone. He stands out like a sore thumb, for he is the only one in the entire street who is carrying anything!*

My fears were quickly realized as several men surrounded the man and took his pallet from him. They appeared to be quite angry.

*Why did Jesus tell him to carry his mat? He could have easily had him leave it behind for some other poor soul in need.*

Looking back at Jesus standing among a sea of desperately needy men and women, I wondered if He would heal all of them. The crowd did not seem to notice Him because their focus was on the pool. They were oblivious to the fact that there was One standing among them who had the power and authority to heal everyone.

Hearing a commotion behind me, I spun around. A rather large crowd had now gathered around the man and his pallet, among them were several Pharisees.

*Jesus creates controversy everywhere He goes.*

I turned to ask Jesus why He had instructed the man to carry his pallet only to discover that He was nowhere to be seen.

"Where did He go?" I asked.

"He was just here," Andrew answered looking around.

"How did He disappear like that?" Matthew asked.

"More importantly, where did He go?" Bartholomew asked.

I responded, "I don't know how He managed to walk away without us seeing Him, but I do know where He has gone. It is Passover, is it not?"

"It is," Thomas answered.

"Therefore, the Master has gone to the temple," I stated.

"Of course!" they exclaimed in unison.

Wasting no time, we hurried to the temple where we found Jesus standing in the midst of the courtyard. Hurrying to His side, I said, "Master, how did You do that? How did You slip away without us seeing You?"

Without responding, He continued searching the crowd. "There he is," He said as He moved through the crowd stopping a short distance from the man who He had just healed. The man was engaged in a very lively conversation with a group of Pharisees. The man turned, and upon seeing Jesus, shouted, "There is the man! He is the one who healed me!"

He then hurried to Jesus' side at which point the Master led him to a secluded corner. The man, his eyes dancing, said, "As I walked down the street carrying my pallet, like You instructed, a man stopped me saying that it was unlawful for me to carry my pallet on the Sabbath.[45] I answered that I was not carrying my pallet in contempt of the Law or the Sabbath. I told them that the Man who healed me told me to carry my pallet. The man asked me who had instructed me to do so, and I told him that I did not know."

Jesus laid His hand on the man's shoulder and said, "You have been healed; do not sin anymore so that nothing worse happens to you."

The man seemed startled by His words. With a nod, he bowed slightly, then spun around and hurried off like a fox running after food. Curious, I followed. The man went straight to the Jewish leaders and said, "Over there, that is the Man who healed me!"

The Master leaned against the wall looking directly at them. One of the leaders, with head held high, marched across the room like a rooster struts through a henhouse. Stopping directly in front of Jesus, he condemned Him for healing the man on the Sabbath and also for telling him to carry his pallet.

Without flinching, Jesus stared directly into the eyes of this prominent man and responded, "My Father is working until now, and I Myself am working. Does not My Father work incessantly for the benefit of mankind? Does He not preserve and govern all God's creatures and all of their actions? Does He not hold the planets in their orbits? Who orders the sun to rise and to set at its appointed time? Who causes the wind to circulate in its appointed course? Does not the tide ebb and flow on the Sabbath as well as every other day of the week?"

Ignoring His point, this prominent man responded, "What! You call God Your Father! How dare You make Yourself equal with God!"

The Pharisee was quickly joined by several others. Jesus calmly answered, "Truly, truly, I say to you, the Son can do nothing of Himself unless it is something He sees the Father doing; for whatever the Father does, these things the Son also does in like manner.

"For the Father loves the Son and shows Him all things that He Himself is doing; and the Father will show Him greater works than the healing of a paralyzed man, so that you will marvel.

"The Father raises the dead and gives life to whom He wishes, for not even the Father judges anyone, but He has given all judgment to the Son so that all will honor the Son even as they honor the Father. He who does not honor the Son does not honor the Father who sent Him.

"Truly, truly I say to you, he who hears My word and believes Him who sent Me, has eternal life and does not come into judgment, but has passed out of death into life.

"Truly, truly, I say to you, an hour is coming and now is, when the dead will hear the voice of the Son of God and those who hear will live.

"Those who do not know my Father are spiritually dead and truly miserable. They are unaware of their misery, which makes them unable to help themselves. The conversion of a soul to God is a resurrection from death to life; then and only then does that soul begin to truly live.

"For just as the Father has life in Himself, even so He gave to the Son also to have life in Himself; and He gave Him authority to execute judgment, because He is the Son of Man.

"Do not marvel at this; for an hour is coming in which all who are in the tombs will hear His voice and will come forth; and those who did the good deeds to a resurrection of life, those who committed the evil deeds to a resurrection of judgment.

"I can do nothing on My own initiative. As I hear, I judge; and My judgment is just because I do not seek My own will, but the will of Him who sent Me.

"If I alone testify about Myself, My testimony is not true. There is another who testifies of Me and I know that the testimony which He gives about Me is true. You have sent to John the baptizer, and He has testified to the truth. The testimony which I receive is not from man, but I say these things so that you may be saved.

"John was the lamp that was burning and was shining, and you were willing to rejoice for a while in his light. You were willing to dance and celebrate about this light, as boys dance around a bonfire. You were fond of him for a time, as little children are fond of a new toy, but you soon grew weary of him and said that he had a demon and now you have him in prison."

The pious men appeared to be unmoved by His words. Jesus continued, "The testimony which I have is greater than the testimony of John; for the works which the Father has given Me to accomplish—the very works that I do prove that the Father has sent Me. And the Father who sent Me has testified of Me.

"You have neither heard His voice at any time nor seen His form. You do not have His word abiding in you, for you do not believe in Him whom He sent.

"You search the Scriptures because you think that in them you have eternal life; it is these that testify about Me. You are unwilling to come to Me so that you may have life, for this is eternal life: to know Me."

Without saying a word, one at a time, the leaders turned and walked away. Jesus followed them shouting, "I do not need the praise of man; it is no addition to My glory. Not only are you ignorant of God, but I know you, that you do not have the love of God abiding in yourselves."

The leaders suddenly stopped. Turning they glared at Jesus; rage filled their eyes.

Without the slightest hesitation, Jesus continued, "I have come in My Father's name, and you do not receive Me. If another comes in his own name, you will receive him.

"How can you believe, when you receive glory from one another and you do not seek the glory that is from the one and only God? You desire to receive praise, and you aim for this in all you do. You give praise to others and applaud them that they might turn and applaud you. The honor that is given to you, you take for yourselves and do not give it to God. It would be well for you to know that ambition and desire for worldly honor are great hindrances to believing in Me.

"Do not think that I will accuse you before the Father; the one who accuses you is Moses, in whom you have set your hope. For if you believed Moses, you would believe Me, for he wrote about Me. But if you do not believe his writings, how will you believe My words?"

Jesus' passionate message appeared to be lost on these men, for they were thoroughly offended and extremely angry. Jesus remained unmoved and looked on with fiery zeal. The men stormed off; killing Him was foremost in their thoughts.[46]

As for me, I was speechless. Jesus was truly amazing. He was the Son of God, but He was also a man with all the natural affections of human nature. He felt pain and pleasure, had a desire to live, had an aversion to suffering and death; yet He never sought His own comfort, neither did He seek to please Himself. He did not live His life according to the pleasure found in people and material things; His ultimate pleasure was found in His Father. He completely submitted himself to His Father's will in all things—He lived for God! I had never known or ever heard of anyone so in love with another that he would completely die to his own desires as completely and fully as Jesus did.

He was truly the Master of all things while living His life as the greatest Servant who would ever live.

# CHAPTER THIRTEEN

The scrubbing of sandals across the stone floor grows louder. The footsteps stop at our door, the key slides into the lock and turns.

*Father, we need more time!*

The heavy metal door groans loudly as it is pushed open. The light from the torch causes great pain to my eyes; I press my face tightly against my forearm.

Relief floods my soul as I hear a familiar voice saying, "Peter, it is Malchus. I have brought you food and drink."

He places the torch in the holder outside the door and pulls the door nearly shut. Hurrying to my side, he holds a wineskin to my mouth, and I drink deeply of his kindness.

"Malchus, it is good to see you, my friend. Is all well with you? And what of your daughter, Miriam? Has she recovered?"

"My soul is at peace, my friend. And my little Miriam once again fills our home with laughter and sunshine. I thank God for healing her; she would have certainly died were it not for the Master's healing touch."

"Oh, Malchus, this is indeed good news that you bring! I thank God with you, my friend. And what of your wife? Has she come to believe in the Messiah?"

"That is the best news of all. Just last week, when I told her how you prayed for our Miriam and that very hour Jesus healed her, she fell into my arms proclaiming that Jesus was indeed the Son of God."

"My cup overflows!" I exclaim only to have Malchus remind me to be quiet lest we are found out.

"Speaking of cups overflowing, take another drink," Malchus says.

My eyes adjust to the light coming through the small opening of the door. I look up into the kind eyes of my friend and brother.

"What have they done to you, Peter?" he asks, gently touching my shoulder. His brow is drawn tight with concern.

"I have merely been through the fire," I answer.

"Your face! Your back! Your chest! Peter, I am sorry," Malchus states as he looks at my wounds.

"Purity is worth the cost, is it not? Did the Lord not say that our works done on earth are either wood, hay, straw, gold, silver or precious stones? Did He not say that we will be purified through fire? 'Tis not a thing to fear, my friend, for the Lord is with us in the fire. He comforts me as I look forward to that glorious day when I will no longer go through times of testing and proving."

"Peter, I will continue to pray for you. And tomorrow, I will try to bring you something to ease your pain. My wife knows of some herbs that will help heal your stripes," Malchus says as he offers me more to drink.

"Thank you, but only come if there is no chance you will be caught. As for the water, would you give the remainder to my fellow prisoners? And, I have no need of bread; please give my portion to them."

"I knew you would say that. That is why I brought extra. Now, take a bite; it will give you the strength you need to finish your course."

He holds the fresh bread to my mouth, and because of the wounds to my face, I find it impossible to bite it. I think back to the last supper I shared with Jesus. He held up the bread and said, "This is My body; eat of it. As often as you do this, remember Me until I come again."

*I remember, Lord. It would be impossible for me to ever forget how You suffered for me, how You loved me.*

Seeing the difficulty I have biting it, Malchus tears off a small piece and places it in my mouth.

"Malchus," I say with my mouth full, "Is it morning or night? One can never tell in this place."

"It is morning," he answers. "I have also come to tell you that your execution has been postponed because Nero has left the city. He ordered that you not be killed until his return. As you well know, he takes great pleasure in tormenting and killing Christians. I am sorry to say that he took a special interest in you, Peter."

I reply, "I rejoice in that the Lord has heard my prayers and has given me more time! You see, Malchus, there are yet those in this cell who need to make certain their eternal home is with Jesus Christ."

"I will join my prayers with yours that they will do so before it is too late," Malchus responds as he places another piece of bread in my mouth. He then turns his attention towards my fellow prisoners and says, "My friends, you would be wise to listen to Peter, for your execution dates have not been postponed."

Turning his attention back to me, he lays his hand on my shoulder and says, "Many are praying for your release, my friend."

"I am ever so grateful for the prayers, and I find great peace in knowing that my heavenly Father will answer according to His perfect will, for my fate lies in the hands of a loving Master in whom I fully trust."

"That is a fact that brings me great comfort and for which all Christians everywhere are eternally grateful," Malchus answers.

"Malchus you have refreshed my body and my soul. May the Lord bless you for the kindness you have shown to me, which placed you in great peril this day."

As he distributes the bread and water to the others, I ask, "Malchus, did I ever tell you that my wife's name is Miriam?"

"You did, Peter. And what an honor it is that my daughter should share the same name as your faithful wife."

"My beloved Miriam was arrested at the same time as I. She stood by my side as Nero sentenced her to die because she would not deny the Lord. As they tore her from my arms, I whispered, 'Miriam, whatever happens, remember the Lord!' She replied, 'Peter, how could I ever forget the One who died to save my life?' Needless to say, Nero was furious and ordered us to be beaten immediately. That was the last time I saw my beautiful wife. What a brave woman she is," I state as sorrow floods my being.

"Peter, I will see what I can find out concerning her," Malchus responds.

"Oh, how wonderful it would be to hear news of her! If she is alive and you see her, please tell her that I love her and pray for her constantly, my friend," I say looking around my cell.

There is just enough light for me to see four men chained. Laban and Justus quickly identify themselves. A third and fourth man who still have not made their identities known are chained on the opposite wall. Malchus offers them bread and water and, without saying a word, they eagerly devour his lifesaving gift.

Justus and Laban look to be quite young, not more than twenty-five years of age. I thank my Father for giving them ears to hear and ask the Holy Spirit to convict them concerning their salvation.

On his way out, Malchus stops at my side and prays for my healing. He says "Peter, may God grant you peace as you finish your race."

"And to you, my friend," I reply.

The door closes, and the thick darkness returns.

After a long silence, a new voice speaks, "My name is Josiah. I just wanted to thank you for asking Malchus to share your bread and water with us. I must admit that I do not understand why you would do such a thing."

"Josiah, I am able to share my water and bread because of the self-sacrificing love of Jesus. He lived this way every day. He was a great Teacher and lived His life according to mercy and kindness and self-sacrifice. I have learned to do the same."

"I have been listening to your story, and I must admit that I am curious about this man you call Jesus. I would like to hear more," Josiah responds.

"I would love nothing more than to share all that I know and will do so, but first let me explain a little about the Jewish leaders and their ways. You see, our rabbis had corrupted many of the commandments by interpreting them more loosely than they were intended and others more strictly. For example, concerning the fourth commandment, which speaks of keeping the Sabbath day holy, they erred in interpreting it too strictly.

"In what happens next, we see Jesus correcting that teaching. He clearly communicates that works of necessity and works of mercy are not only lawful on the Sabbath, but are to be desired."

# CHAPTER FOURTEEN

The day after Jesus healed the lame man and confronted the Pharisees in the temple, we left Jerusalem and turned towards Galilee. We journeyed for six days when, on the Sabbath, Jesus led us through a grain field. We were hungry, so we picked the heads of grain. It was allowed, for the Law clearly permitted this courtesy even on the Sabbath.[47]

It was a pitiful meal, if you could call it that, but no one complained. Well, there were some who complained, but they were not among our number. You see, the Pharisees, who often traveled with us, watched the Master's every move. Eagerly, like vultures discovering what appears to be a victim, they hurried to Jesus' side and said, "Look at Your disciples!"

The Master turned His attention toward us for just a moment, then looked back at the Pharisees saying nothing. The eldest Pharisee continued, "Do You not see what they are doing? They are reaping and threshing grain on the Sabbath!"

Jesus plucked some heads of grain. Rubbing it between His hands, He answered, "Have you not read the story of what David did when he became hungry? Have you not read how he and his companions entered the house of God and ate the consecrated bread, which was not lawful for him to eat nor for those with him, but for the priests alone? David ate because he was hungry.

"Have you not read in the Law that on the Sabbath the priests in the temple did a great deal of work, which in a common case would have been desecrating the Sabbath, but in this case they broke the Sabbath and were innocent because the temple service required and justified it.

"But I say to you that Someone greater than the temple is here. If the temple service justified what the priests did in their service, then My disciples are justified even more so as they attend to Me. The Son of Man, in a grain field, is greater than the temple.

"But if you had known what this means, 'I desire mercy and not sacrifice,' you would not have condemned the innocent. The Sabbath was made for man, and not man for the Sabbath. The Son of Man is Lord even of the Sabbath. The Sabbath was meant to be a blessing to man, not a burden. It was intended to be a day given by God in mercy to man—a day of rest for the body and worship unto God."[48]

The Pharisees made no response. They were visibly angry and unusually silent. Throwing up their hands, they stormed away.

Jesus plucked another handful of grain; we followed His example. Resuming our journey I said, "Teacher, it is becoming obvious to me that the Pharisees do an injustice to the Law by creating numerous petty rules for its observance, which does not help us to observe it, but on the contrary it makes the Law appear harsh, undesirable and impossible to keep."

"Peter, I did not come to destroy the Law, but to fulfill it," he responded.

"What?" I asked.

"I did not come to destroy the Law the way some of the Pharisees have by teaching it incorrectly. I have come to fulfill it by teaching it correctly."

We walked on in silence thinking about the Pharisees. The stricter Jews fast two days a week from sun-up to sunset. Many whiten their faces and wear clothing that is dishevelled so that everyone will know that they are fasting. Much of what they do is for the sake of appearance. The outside of the cup might appear clean while the inside is polluted.

*I have lived my whole life this way.*

Three days later, we arrived in Galilee where Jesus quickly set about teaching the people. On the Sabbath, as was the Master's custom, we went to the synagogue. Once inside, I saw the same Pharisees who condemned us for picking the grain. Pulling Jesus aside, I whispered, "Master, this is the synagogue of the Pharisees who condemned us."

"I am aware of that," He answered.

"I do not think we are welcome here."

"That does not matter, Simon."

"But?"

"All is well, My friend," Jesus responded.

Jesus sat down and began to teach; the people quickly gathered around Him. The Sanhedrin sat in their usual places of honor in the center front. From this vantage point, they could easily deal with anyone who might try to lead the people astray or teach false doctrine.

The Pharisees glared at Jesus with eyes of steel, like hungry lions waiting to pounce on a weak prey. They had one thing on their minds and one thing only and that was to catch Jesus in error and expose Him, destroying Him if possible.

As Jesus taught, His gaze continually fell on a man whose right hand was withered and was completely useless.

The Sanhedrin leaned forward, beads of perspiration formed on their brows.

*I wonder if the Master knows how dangerous this situation is.*

Just then Jesus turned to the man with the withered hand and said, "Friend, come up here!"

The man, clearly unsure as to what he should do, looked at his neighbor who encouraged him by pushing him forward. He made his way to the front of the crowd. He was indeed a pitiful sight. His paralyzed hand was nothing but skin and bones, absolutely useless. It was obvious by his appearance that this man was extremely poor.

At this point, one of the Sanhedrin, a Pharisee, stepped forward. Waving his arms, he cleared his throat and asked, "Is it lawful to heal on the Sabbath?"

Jesus faced the Pharisee and responded, "Let me ask you a

question. Is it lawful to do good or to do harm on the Sabbath? Is it lawful to save a life or to destroy it?"

The man refused to respond.

*Jesus appears angry, why?*

I looked at the religious leaders; their faces were set like flint, hard and cold like a block of ice. It was obvious that their hearts were unmoved by this man's hopeless and sad predicament. I now understood the reason for Jesus' anger—these men were stubborn, blind and hardhearted. They did not want to know the truth; they were perfectly content with life the way it was.

Jesus continued, "What man is there among you who has a sheep and if it falls into a ditch on the Sabbath, will you not take hold of it and lift it out?"

*Every man in this place would rescue his sheep. I have done so myself on several occasions.*

The Master's voice trembled, "How much more valuable is a man than a sheep?"

Again, no response.

Undaunted, Jesus said, "Men are a great deal better and much more valuable than the finest of creatures. Therefore, it is lawful, dutiful and most reasonable to do good on the Sabbath day."

Turning His attention back to the man who stood with his head down and his eyes fixed on the floor, Jesus, with great tenderness, said, "Sir, stretch out your hand."

As he did, his hand was perfectly restored, just like the other. The crowd came alive, buzzing with excitement, but the Pharisees were filled with rage and rushed out of the synagogue.[49]

I turned to Andrew and Matthew and whispered, "I have learned this day that doing good is not to be left undone out of fear of offending another."

"Indeed," Matthew replied.

Andrew said, "Jesus is in serious trouble now, for the Jewish Law states that medical attention could only be given on the Sabbath if a life was in danger. This man's life was not in danger and the Pharisees are furious."

"But, Andrew, we must take into account that the Master knew they would respond this way, and He healed the man anyway. Besides He knows the Law better than anyone," I responded.

At this point, Jesus walked up and said, "The Sanhedrin have gone to the Herodians to conspire against Me as to how they might destroy Me. Come, let us withdraw from here and go to the sea."

We quickly followed as did a great number of people from Galilee, Judea, Jerusalem, Idumea and beyond the Jordan. Even people from the vicinity of Tyre and Sidon made up the Master's following, for word about His exploits had traveled far.

From Jerusalem, we traveled to village after village. The sick and diseased pushed through the crowds eager to get near Jesus that they might touch Him. Jesus healed many and cast out many unclean spirits. Often, the unclean spirits would cry out, "You are the Son of God!" But, each time, Jesus commanded them to be silent and ordered them to leave the person, which they did in every instance.

Throughout our journey, I often found myself thinking about the difference between Jesus and other rabbis I had known. To the Pharisees, religion was a ritual, which meant obeying certain rules and regulations. Because Jesus broke some of their rules, they determined that He was evil. But, religion, to Jesus, was about loving God and others.

With each passing day, it became more obvious that I needed to make a lot of changes in my life.

We arrived in a small village near the edge of the sea of Galilee. In a very short time, the whole village came out to meet the Master. As the multitude saw the miracles happening right before their eyes, they pushed in so close that Jesus was pressed from every side, making it nearly impossible for Him to move. Stretching out His arm, He tugged on Andrew's sleeve, shouting, "You and James go ahead of us and get the boats ready."

The two young men pushed their way through the mob eager to serve the Master.

As Jesus healed the sick, He warned them not to tell others who He was because He still had much to do. With great effort, we pushed through the people toward the sea.

Trying my best to shield the Master from the pressing throng, I shouted over the noise of the crowd to Andrew who stood beside me, "I have never seen a day like this in Israel."

Andrew replied, "Is this not what Isaiah the prophet spoke of when he prophesied concerning the Son of Man saying, 'Here is My servant whom I have chosen, the One I love, in whom I delight. I am very pleased with Him. I will put My Spirit upon Him. He will announce justice to the Gentiles. He will fulfill His work without yelling or arguing; no one will hear His voice in the streets. He will not break the stem of a plant that has been bent. He will not put out the flame of a wick which is barely burning, until He causes justice to win. The nations will put their hope in His name.' Simon, I believe this is what Isaiah was speaking about so long ago!"

His words rang true.

*There is so much more to the Master than I know.*

"Have you ever known any other rabbi of Israel to so completely embrace weak, uneducated, immature, people like us?" I asked.

"No, Simon, I have not. This prophet was cut from a different cloth. He does not reject any but extends mercy and grace to all. Upon seeing a bruised reed, He does not tread upon it neither does He break it, but instead, He embraces it, supporting it until it becomes as strong as the trees of Lebanon. The candle that has only been recently lit, though it smokes and does not flame, He does not blow out, but waits patiently for it to burn again, encouraging it all the while. Truly, there has never been another like this One!"[50]

# CHAPTER FIFTEEN

Someone approaches our cell. The door slowly opens, which is a good sign. The torch is left outside, another good sign. Malchus whispers, "It is Malchus. I have brought ointment for your infection."

Wasting no time, he quickly yet gently covers my painful wounds with the soothing medicine.

"I am ever so grateful, my friend," I whisper.

"Peter, I am afraid that I have distressing news. It seems that our friend and brother Tiberias has been arrested. Word got out that he has been helping the Christian prisoners. When he was interrogated, he boldly shared the good news. Enraged, the centurion ordered that he be flogged and thrown into your old cell.

"I will do all that I can for him, but they have beaten him so severely that, without a miracle, I do not believe he will live through the night."

My heart is pained at this news. Tiberias has been so good to me, faithful to the Lord and a true servant to many. "This is distressing news, my friend. I will certainly pray for our friend and brother. It is reassuring to know that God alone determines a man's destiny."

Malchus replies, "Peter, I am afraid that my faith is not as strong as yours. I had trouble sleeping last night for wondering if I could endure such abuse."

I respond, "With your affections set upon the Lord, you can run over a wall and leap over a troop; you can suffer persecution and overcome Satan by the blood of the Lamb and the word of your testimony. Love never fails, my friend. It is important to remember that Satan is limited to only what God allows. Therefore, if God allows you to suffer, He will use it for good in your life if you will let Him. He will walk with you through it.

"Life is filled with many storms. There are times when God calms the storm, and there are times when He allows the storm to rage and He calms the child. There are times when He sends an angel to open the prison doors like He did for me nearly thirty years ago. And then there are the times when He keeps the prison door shut, but He continually gives me the grace I need to endure hardship.

"God is in control, my friend. If it is not God's will for Tiberias to die, then he will live, but that does not mean that we do nothing. We shall pray, for the effective prayer of a righteous man can accomplish much."

"Peter, I long to have faith like yours."

"You are a man in love, my friend. Your faith and your love for the Lord will keep you."

"I hope you are right," Malchus responds as he applies the last of the ointment.

"Malchus, I want to thank you for all that you have done for me and so many others. Be sure to thank your wife for her kindness as well. Your rewards will be great. But, go now and please do not risk your life by coming to me again. It is much too dangerous."

"I will come as I can. I might fear suffering and persecution, but I do not fear death, Peter, for you have taught me well. Farewell, my brother. Lord willing, I shall come again soon."

I pray for Tiberias for hours. And then it happens— I am filled with perfect peace. I have the strongest impression that Tiberias is no longer on this earth but has entered his eternal home. I feel both joy and sorrow. Joy because he is free from pain and suffering and sorrow because I long to be where he is.

"Justus, Laban, Josiah are you awake?" I whisper.

"Indeed we are," the three answer.

"I am awake as well," echoes another voice.

"And who might you be?" I ask.

"I am Eleazar, the son of John, a Jewish brother."

"Eleazar, my brother, I am so happy to make your acquaintance. But I must say that even though Justus, Laban and Josiah are Gentiles, they are my brothers also."

"That cannot be! No Gentile shall ever be my brother! You and I are God's chosen people, a royal priesthood, a holy nation. God forbid that you would equate these Gentiles to be likened to us!" Eleazar arrogantly exclaims.

"Eleazar, Jesus came to save not only the Jews, but also the Gentiles. He is no respecter of persons and is not willing that any should perish, but that all should know Him. We are the branches; Jesus is the vine. Gentiles are grafted into the vine when they come to know Jesus as their Savior, making them fellow brothers and sisters. Jesus went to the cross so that all men could have their sins forgiven, for He desires a relationship with us."

Josiah interrupts, his voice trembling, "Peter, I believe that Jesus is the Son of God, and I have no problem admitting that I am a sinner who desperately needs a Savior. From this day forth, for as long as I shall live, I will live for Jesus!"

"Welcome to the family of God, my friend and brother, your sins are forgiven, and you are clean and free. Today is a brand new day for you. Your past has been washed away, and today salvation has come to you," I exclaim.

"Is that it? Is it that simple? Is that all I have to do to be saved?" Josiah asks.

"Salvation is easy; walking it out is the difficult part. You see, Jesus paid the price for your sins on a cross thus simplifying, if you will, salvation. He became the criminal and paid the ransom price to set you free. You are now free from your sins. Your body may be locked in chains, but your spirit is perfectly clean, white as snow and absolutely free. There will be no chains in eternity; you will live in perfect Light surrounded by perfect love and peace. No more tears, no more sorrow, no more sin, no more striving. We will be an eternal partner, likened unto a bride, to Jesus who is the Son of God. We will rule and reign with Him."

Eleazar interrupts, his voice filled with anger, "I can not understand how you can betray our people by teaching such heresy!"

I reply, "My greatest sorrow and shame would be that I would betray the One who died to bring us this good news. If you think that I betray my people, then you do not understand the message that I bring. Eleazar, I love the Jewish people and earnestly desire for them to know the Messiah—that they might walk in the fullness of their destiny."

Justus interrupts, "Peter, perhaps you could tell us more, and in the hearing, Eleazar might come to understand? Perhaps I am being selfish, but I am eager to hear it all, to the finish and I am well aware that I have so very little time left."

"You are right, Justus," I reply. "Eleazar, I could argue with you all day long, and it would mean nothing, but there is power in the good news, and that is exactly what you need. You need to hear the truth, and the truth is a Man not a set of rules and regulations, my friend."

"You do not know what you are saying. You are deceived, tricked and have become a lunatic!" Eleazar exclaims.

"Eleazar, when I saw Jesus boldly confront our religious leaders, it completely changed the way I thought of religion and it opened my eyes to the reality of His message. It was then that the other disciples and I learned a valuable lesson that proved very necessary for what we would be called to endure in the years ahead. As we watched Jesus suffer ridicule, rejection and persecution and still remain true to God, our hearts were profoundly impacted. And in doing so, He instilled in us the ability to bear up under persecution and isolation and the suffering that the prince of this world loves to inflict upon those whose hearts are burning with devotion and dedication. Persecution only serves to strengthen a lovesick heart, if you allow it to do so, my friend.

"After Jesus died and was resurrected, John and I were arrested and brought before the Sanhedrin. Because of our confidence and boldness, they recognized us as being companions of Jesus. The only reason we were able to stand before them unafraid was because of the example Jesus set for us. We saw Him stand for righteousness against powerful leaders, and in every situation, He did what was right, not what would tickle the ears of those listening, neither did He do the thing that was easy. He disregarded the popular message of the hour and spoke truth enduring whatever criticism came as a result."

"I am such a coward, Peter, I could never willingly endure suffering if I had a way out. I could not do what you are doing," Josiah answers.

"With God on your side and a heart filled with love, my friend, you would be surprised at what you can endure," I answer.

"Then tell me more, I must know more, for I long to love Him more!" Josiah cries out.

# CHAPTER SIXTEEN

We finally arrived at the Sea where Andrew and James waited on the bow of the boat for us. Leaving the multitude behind, we eagerly climbed in. With the wind in our favor, we were out to sea ever so quickly. Jesus instructed us to follow the coastline.

It was so delightful to be alone with Jesus, away from the never ending demands and constant clamoring of the people. I thoroughly enjoyed the sea air, the endless blue sky, the gentle rocking of the boat and the personal attention of the Master.

*I could stay here, in this boat, on the sea, with Jesus, forever.*

"Master, if we were to never leave this boat, I would be content," I said.

"Peter, never be content with less than what your Father has planned for you. There is a very real danger that you will be satisfied with a little love, a little power, a little authority. Will you contend for the fullness?," He responded.

"But I am satisfied," I replied.

"How is it that you are satisfied with a little when there is so much more for you, for all of you? Never be content until you are walking in the fullness of Who I am and all that I have for you. Satan would have you satisfied with a little, but I would have you desperate for more until the gospel is preached in all the earth."

"How is such a thing possible?"

"Absolutely nothing is impossible for Me," He answered and then pointed to the shoreline of Capernaum and instructed us to dock there.

The sun was setting, so we quickly found a suitable place to camp. Matthew and I collected wood and dried dung for a fire while Thomas and Judas got water from a nearby spring.

Before the fire was even lit, people began arriving from all directions, for news had spread rapidly that Jesus had returned. The Master eagerly welcomed them and with great joy taught the people and healed their sick.

After several hours, He dismissed them and returned to our campfire where we dined on salted fish and bread. Afterwards, John pulled out his flute and began to play. I walked to the edge of our campsite, which was on the brink of a hill. I looked out across the broad, open field where hundreds of small campfires lit up the darkness. A multitude of tiny sparks danced their way heavenward. John played as the others sang, "O Lord, our Lord, how majestic is Your name in all the earth! You have displayed Your splendor above the heavens...."

Their words faded into the background as I focused on the scene before me. The fire light, the darkness, the sparks flying, the crackling of the flames.

*What is it about this scene that makes it so beautiful to me?*

Unaware that Jesus had come up behind me, I jumped when He laid His hand on my shoulder. "I didn't know you were there," I said.

"I am *always* here, Peter," He responded.

"Are those just words or are they really true?"

"It is really true," He answered looking out across the field. "It is beautiful, is it not?" He asked.

"I was just thinking that," I replied.

"Simon Peter, do you remember the words of Isaiah when he said, 'The Land of Zebulun and the land of Naphtali, by the way of the sea, beyond the Jordan, Galilee of the Gentiles, the people who were sitting in darkness saw a great light, and to those who were sitting in the land and shadow of death, upon them a light dawned.'"[51]

"I remember," I responded.

"Simon, I am the Light that he spoke of. What you see stretched out before you looks very similar to what happens in the human heart when I am received and embraced as the Truth."

"Light always consumes darkness," I stated.

"That is why I have come," Jesus added.

"But the fire will go out without constant attention," I observed.

"Exactly. Peter, I did not come to gather servants, I came because of love, for I desire to love and to be loved. I desire relationship, not merely servanthood. I desire your heart. Being a disciple of Mine is not only about learning and training and serving and obeying, but it is first and foremost about knowing Me intimately. You see, Peter, I know that if I can win your heart, you will do whatever I ask, and you will do so because you love Me not just because it is the right thing to do. Our relationship is like this fire, which, if not given close attention, will soon grow dim and will eventually die."

"My love for You will never die," I responded.

With a gentle embrace, the Master responded, "You are greatly loved, Peter."

"Master, who am I that You would love me so?"

"You are Peter, the rock. I chose you before the foundation of the world."

"Sometimes I am really afraid that I will never be good enough for You. After all, You are so perfect and good," I responded.

"You need never fear that I will not love you, for My love is like the sun—fierce, all-consuming and ever so constant. It shines down on both My friends and My enemies. My love does not pick and choose; it is not a respecter of persons. My love consumes darkness and warms the cold heart. It encircles you, guards you and guides you. I am patient, kind, meek and lowly in heart. I do not seek My own, neither am I provoked. I do not take into account a wrong suffered neither do I rejoice in unrighteousness, but I rejoice with the truth. My love bears all things, believes all things, hopes all things and endures all things. Love never fails. But now abides faith, hope and love, but the greatest of these is love, Peter. Know that I will always love you. My love is a gift that you cannot earn neither can you keep Me from bestowing it upon you, My friend."[52]

"I have never known a love like this," I replied.

With the slightest chuckle, He responded, "And to think that you have only just begun to know Me."

With a final embrace, He rejoined the others.

With much to think about, I decided to walk through the multitude of people camped before me. I stopped to listen as they shared story after story of the great exploits of the Master. He was even more popular than I realized, and many were talking about making Him king.

When I returned to our campsite, John was still playing his flute, Thomas and James played their goatskin drums while the others sang and danced except for Judas; he was fast asleep.

Warming myself by the fire, I watched. My heart overflowed with great affection for the Master, yet, at the same time, my thoughts were in turmoil. Was He really who He declared Himself to be? I looked through the flames at the Master who danced around the fire and whispered to myself, "Just who are You?" I was constantly plagued with that question and never stopped asking it because Jesus was such a mystery to me.

*Just when I think I understand Him, He does something so extravagant that I have to reevaluate what I believed. His love is constant, but He certainly is unpredictable.*

Having thoroughly exhausted Himself, Jesus bid us good-night and slipped away into the darkness. I knew where He was going; He was going to spend most of His night in prayer.

A little before sunrise, His voice awakened me, "Simon Peter, come with Me."

Rubbing my eyes, I sat up and watched as He woke Andrew, James, John, Philip, Bartholomew, Matthew, Thomas, James the son of Alphaeus, Simon the Zealot, Judas the son of James and Judas.

A sleepy yet curious twelve followed Jesus through the darkness to a clearing on the hillside. The Master sat down in the manner of a Rabbi who was about to deliver an important message, yet He said not a word; He merely looked at the horizon. Like a group of school children, we sat quietly at first but quickly grew impatient. "Master, why have

You brought us here?" I asked jumping to my feet.

"It is beautiful, is it not?" He responded as He pointed to the sunrise.

I began pacing as did Judas. "My love is like the sun," the Master quietly reminded me.

Stopping, I turned and looked at the bright, red ball of fire rising from the sea. Its brilliant rays drove out the darkness and warmed my face.

*It is beautiful, more beautiful than I realized.*

I sat back down while Judas continued pacing. Once the sun was fully up, the Master turned to James then to John and said, "You two are the sons of thunder."

I almost laughed aloud. This was the best description of these two I had ever heard. We grew up together, and they have always been fiery, fervent and impulsive. When it came to justice these two were unstoppable.

Jesus motioned for Judas to stop his pacing and sit with us. He then went around the circle calling each of us by name. "Simon, who is called Peter and your brother, Andrew, Philip, Bartholomew, Thomas, Matthew, James, the son of Alphaeus, Thaddaeus, Simon the zealot and Judas Iscariot."

*What is He doing?*

He said, "I have chosen you to be much more than disciples. I have chosen you to be My apostles, those who are called out, My sent ones. I am setting you apart. Others will come and go, but you are to remain with Me, identifying your life with Mine.

"My desire is that you might know Me, for in knowing Me, you will know God. I came to reveal My Father's nature and character to you. I came to show you that He is not a distant, angry God, but He is gracious and compassionate, slow to anger, abounding in lovingkindness and relenting of evil.[53]

"I came to bring light to a dark and dying world."

His words overwhelmed me even though I did not understand much of it. As for His statement about knowing Him, I was completely baffled, for we already knew Him. We knew Him to be a brilliant, gifted

Teacher of Israel, a Healer and a Prophet. And what was this talk of knowing God?

*Everyone knows that it is impossible to know God, for God is much too holy for anyone to come near, much less to know intimately.*

Jesus looked at me and smiled.

*He knows what I am thinking...again.*

With a nod, He said, "There is nothing hidden that I do not see. Now, let us return to the multitude."

As we walked the rocky path, I looked around at Jesus' little group of—what did He call us? Apostles, that was it. It was amazing that Jesus had chosen a band of mostly young, illiterate commoners, utterly devoid of social standing to be His closest friends. Several of us were Galileans, uneducated and untrained men. And then there was Matthew, the famous tax collector, and also Simon the Zealot who had been part of a band of violent nationalists who pledged to commit murder, if necessary, in order to rid Israel of its foreign rulers. To be certain, judging by worldly standards, we had nothing to offer the Master except for one thing and that was our affection and devotion, which was easy for me because I already loved the Master.[54]

Having lagged behind, Jesus stopped, waiting for me to catch up. Placing His arm around my shoulder, He said, "Peter, I chose you because I love you. You are perfectly suited for Me as are the others. It does not matter to Me your social position or your education or lack thereof. Neither am I concerned with your previous history; that is not what qualifies you to be Mine. Neither do I look upon the outward circumstances of a man in order to determine his value or usefulness. On the contrary, I look within; I look at a man's heart. I look for that yes in his heart, for that desire to please Me. Does that mean that I expect him to be perfect? Absolutely not, but it does mean that he will pursue holiness, for I am holy."

"Will I ever be like You?" I asked feeling lower than the rocks.

"Peter, have no fear, for I am faithful to complete what I have begun. You just keep pursuing Me and I will chisel away at those things that prevent you from one hundred percent obedience," He answered then hurried ahead to speak with John.

*Maybe it really is true. Maybe He really is the Messiah, the King who will deliver us from the evil clutches of Rome.*

I stopped.

*He has chosen twelve apostles and there are twelve tribes in Israel. If He is the Messiah, then He will set up His Kingdom in Jerusalem and will appoint men to rule over the twelve tribes. This must be why He has chosen us! It all makes sense now—we are going to rule and reign with Him!*

My heart raced at the thought.

I hurried to catch up with John and the Master. Jesus looked at me, and His whole face lit up.

*Is this man the King, the Messiah?*

Jesus threw His arm around my shoulder, and we continued on. His eyes were filled with life. Jesus was indeed very intriguing. His wisdom went far beyond that of Solomon, His kindness far surpassed that of Ruth and His courage was greater than king David's.

*I am glad I decided to be His disciple.*

Because of my fascination with Jesus, I was only vaguely aware of my surroundings, so I was surprised at how quickly we arrived at the crest of the hill that overlooked Capernaum, which was about two miles away. But, Capernaum was not what captured my attention; it was the fact that the valley between us and Capernaum was filled with an ocean of people—so many that is was frightening.

"What ever shall we do?" I asked the Master.

"We will climb the mountain," He answered as He pointed to the small mountain to our left.

"Climb the mountain?" I whispered to no one in particular then quickly scrambled after the Master.

We followed as Jesus led the way. When the multitude recognized Jesus, without hesitation, they followed us up the rocky terrain. About halfway up, Jesus stopped on a large rock platform and sat down. He called the twelve of us to His side. Like children sitting at the feet of their father, we gathered around Him.

From this perspective, I could see for miles and the view was stunning! The sky was a clear, crisp blue with a few clouds scattered here and there. At the foot of the mountain, the large, open valley was adorned with patches of dark green grass and a multitude of very colorful wildflowers. The waters of the sea of Galilee glistened under the sun like a field of emeralds. And nestled between the sea and the foot of this mountain was Capernaum.

I looked at Jesus; He was staring at that little fishing town. His eyes spoke volumes.

"Oh, Capernaum, if you only knew that there was One gazing upon you that has the words of life, you would surely bow down to Him," I whispered in the wind.

*Jesus is passionate about all that He does and all that He sees. Never have I known anyone to have so much zeal for life and such endless love for people as the Master has. I wish that I could live and love in this same way.*

The same eyes of love that gazed upon Capernaum now turned to the sea of needy people sitting before Him. He lifted His voice; His words filled the mountainside, echoing off the surrounding rocks and allowing even those furthest away to hear.

*He has brought us here knowing that in this place He would be heard by all! Not only is He kind, compassionate and loving, but He is also brilliant!*

The Master began, "Blessed are the poor in spirit, those who have come to depend upon God for everything, for theirs is the Kingdom of heaven! Happy, blessed are those who mourn, for they shall be comforted! Blessed are the gentle, those who humbly wait on God, for they shall inherit the earth! Happy and blessed are those who hunger and thirst for righteousness, for they shall be satisfied! Blessed are the merciful, for they shall receive mercy!

"Happy and blessed are the pure in heart, those who recognize that God alone is their help and reward, those whose desire is to walk in holiness, for they shall see God! How happy and blessed are the peacemakers, for they shall be called sons of God! Happy and blessed are those who have been persecuted for the sake of righteousness, for theirs is the Kingdom of heaven!

"Blessed are you when people insult you and persecute you, and tell all kinds of vicious lies about you because you follow Me! Be glad in that day and leap for joy, for behold, your reward is great in heaven. For in the same way their fathers treated the prophets of old.

"You are the salt of the earth; but if the salt has become tasteless, how can it be made salty again? A disciple who does not live according to the principles of the Kingdom is worth about as much as tasteless salt. That salt is no longer good for anything, except to be thrown out and trampled under foot by men.

"You are the light of the world."

*Of course we are. The Jews are God's chosen people and Israel is the light of the world.*

"A city set on a hill cannot be hidden; nor does anyone light a lamp and put it under a basket. Instead, they place it on the lampstand so that it gives light to all who are in the house. My friends, live your life in such a way that your light shines before men so that they may see your good works and glorify your Father who is in heaven."

I looked around at the crowd. They looked as proud as I felt.

*They like this Preacher!*

The Master said, "Do not think that I came to abolish the Law or the Prophets; I did not come to abolish, but to complete it and interpret it correctly. For truly I say to you until heaven and earth pass away, not the smallest letter or the tiniest stroke shall pass from the Law, not until everything that must happen has happened. Whoever then does not obey even one of the least of these commandments and teaches others to do the same, shall be called least in the Kingdom of heaven; but whoever keeps and teaches them, he shall be called great in the Kingdom of heaven.

"For I say to you that unless your righteousness surpasses that of the Scribes and Pharisees, you will not enter the Kingdom of heaven."

Jesus paused.

*What? The Scribes and Pharisees are the most respected religious people in all of Israel. How can anyone surpass them? There is not enough hours in the day to do so!*

Once the people settled down, the Master continued, "You have heard it said that the ancients were told, 'You shall not commit murder,' and 'Whoever commits murder shall be liable to the court.'

"But I say to you that anyone who is angry with his brother shall be guilty before the court of heaven. Whoever says to his brother, 'You are stupid,' shall be guilty before the Supreme court. And whoever calls someone 'fool,' thus insulting his character shall be guilty enough to go into the fiery hell.

"My friends, you have believed that murder is the act of taking the life of another, but I say to you that the very attitude of speaking against your brother or your enemy is equal to the act of murder."

I was growing increasingly uncomfortable.

"When you deal with another in anger, you open the door for a spirit of murder, and before you realize it, your weakness turns into a prison and you will pay a great price in that place."

The Master's face was filled with great love; his eyes were filled with passion.

*He cares so deeply for us! I do not believe I could hear this message if it were not for His obvious affection.*

"If you are presenting your offering at the altar, and remember that your brother has something against you, do not wait for him to come to you. Instead, leave your offering at the altar and go find your brother. Once you have reconciled with him then you can return and present your offering.

"Make friends quickly with your opponent while you are with him on the way to court so that your enemy may not hand you over to the judge, and the judge to the officer, and you be thrown into prison. Truly, I say to you, you will not come out of there until you have paid everything you owe down to the last cent.

"Friends, do not allow anger to go uncontested in your life. If you allow anger, offense or unforgiveness to remain they will grow into a stronghold that will imprison you.

*Never have I thought it wrong to be angry with my friend, much less my enemy. I certainly never considered it equal to murder!*

His words were absolutely shocking not only to me, but also to the multitude.

"You have heard that it was said, 'You shall not commit adultery.' But I say to you that everyone who looks at a woman with lust for her has already committed adultery with her in his heart.

"If your right eye makes you stumble, tear it out and throw it from you; for it is better for you to lose one of the parts of your body, than for your whole body to be thrown into hell.

"If your right hand makes you stumble, cut it off and throw it from you; for it is better for you to lose one of the parts of your body, than for your whole body to go into hell. In other words, do whatever you must do to flee the worldly lusts that war against you! Be radical in your pursuit of holiness and purity! Wage war against immorality, My friends. Get violent about overcoming immorality."

*Now this is really over the edge! Who can live this way?*

"It was said, 'Whoever sends his wife away, let him give her a certificate of divorce.' But I say to you that everyone who divorces his wife, except for the reason of unfaithfulness, makes her commit adultery; and whoever marries a divorced woman commits adultery.

*This is certainly contrary to the custom of the day. Many rabbis and also Roman law allow divorce for almost any reason. There are a few who allow it only if the wife was unfaithful.*

"Again, you have heard that the ancients were told, 'You shall not make false vows, but shall fulfill your vows to the Lord.' But I say to you, make no oath at all, either by heaven, for it is the throne of God, or by the earth, for it is the footstool of His feet, or by Jerusalem, for it is the city of the great King.

"Neither should you make an oath by your head, for you cannot make one hair white or black. But let your 'Yes' be a simple 'Yes,' and your 'No' be a simple, 'No.' Anything beyond this has its origin in evil. After all, everything by which you can swear ultimately belongs to God anyway. Therefore, live in such a way that you are as good as your word; walk in integrity.

"You have heard that our fathers were told, 'An eye for an eye, and a tooth for a tooth.' But I say to you, do not stand against a person who does you wrong. On the contrary, if someone slaps you on your right cheek, turn the other to him also. If anyone wants to sue you and take your shirt, let him have your coat also."

*In our culture a blow on the right cheek is the most grievous insult possible, apart from inflicting serious physical injury. How could I ever respond to such an insult in this manner?*

"Whoever forces you to go one mile, go with him two. Give to him who asks of you and do not turn away from him who wants to borrow from you."

*This is unheard of! It is only human nature to resist anyone who tries to force another to serve them.*

"You have heard that it was said, 'You shall love your neighbor and hate your enemy.' But I say to those of you who are listening, love your enemies; do good to those who hate you; pray for those who persecute you. Bless those who curse you; pray for those who mistreat you.

"Give to everyone who asks of you, and whoever takes away what is yours, do not demand it back.

"Treat others the same way you want them to treat you. If you love those who love you, what credit is that to you? For even sinners love those who love them. If you do good to those who do good to you, what credit is that to you? For even sinners do the same. If you lend to those from whom you expect to receive, what credit is that to you? Even sinners lend to sinners in order to receive back the same amount.

"If you greet only your brothers, only those you enjoy, what more are you doing than others? Do not even the Gentiles do the same? Should your lives not look differently from sinners? Of course you should! Therefore, you are to be like your heavenly Father who is merciful and perfect. Love your enemies, and do good. Lend, expecting nothing in return and your reward will be great and you will be sons of the Most High; for He Himself is kind to ungrateful and evil men. Be merciful, just as your Father is merciful."

*Love my enemies? Don't demand back what is taken from me? Do good to those who hate me? Bless those who curse me? Lend, expecting nothing in return? Surely, He can't mean it?*

"I am speaking about living your life in absolute, complete unselfishness because of love. My friends, I am calling you to value relationships above all else and to regard possessions as nothing in comparison."

*This is absolutely unheard of!*

"Beware of practicing your righteousness before men for the purpose of being noticed by them; otherwise, you have no reward with your Father who is in heaven."

I looked across the crowd at a small group of Pharisees standing nearby with their arms tightly folded across their chests.

*They certainly aren't very happy right now.*

Jesus stepped down from the platform and picked up a small child who had wandered away from her mother. Smoothing her hair, wiping her tears, He continued, "When you give to the poor, do not sound a trumpet before you, as the hypocrites do in the synagogues and in the streets, so that they may be honored by men. Truly I say to you, if the praise of man is what you want then that is what you will receive, that will be your reward.

"But, when you give to the poor, do not let your left hand know what your right hand is doing, so that your giving will be in secret; and your Father who sees what is done in secret will reward you."

He placed the child in her mother's waiting arms only to find a little boy tugging on His robe. With a chuckle He lifted him high in the air, which caused the little one to squeal with delight.

Walking among the people with the little boy still in His arms, He said, "When you pray, do not be like the hypocrites; for they love to stand and pray in the synagogues and on the street corners so that they may be seen by men. Truly I say to you, they have their reward in full. But when you pray, go into your inner room, close your door and pray to your Father who is in secret, and your Father who sees what is done in secret will reward you.

"And when you are praying, do not use meaningless repetition as the Gentiles do, for they suppose that they will be heard for their many words. My friends, do not be like them; for your Father knows what you need before you ask Him. Effective prayer is a result of a personal, intimate relationship with your Father who delights in meeting the needs of His children. Prayer is not a business partnership, but a child speaking with his or her heavenly Father. Therefore, pray this way:

"Our Father who is in heaven,
Hallowed by Your name. Your Kingdom come.
Your will be done on earth as it is in heaven.
Give us this day our daily bread.
And forgive our sins as we also
 have forgiven those who have sinned against us.
And do not lead us into temptation,
 but deliver us from evil.
For yours is the Kingdom and the power and
 the glory forever. Amen.

"If you forgive others for their transgressions, your heavenly Father will also forgive you. But if you do not forgive others, then your Father will not forgive your transgressions.

"Whenever you fast, do not put on a gloomy face as the hypocrites do, for they neglect their appearance when they are fasting so that they will be noticed by men. Truly I say to you, that is their reward and they have it in full. But you, when you fast, anoint your head and wash your face so that your fasting will not be noticed by men but by your Father who sees in secret; and your Father who sees what is done in secret will reward you.

"Do not store up for yourselves treasures on earth, where moth and rust destroy, and where thieves break in and steal. But store up for yourselves treasures in heaven, where neither moth nor rust destroys, and where thieves do not break in or steal; for where your treasure is, there your heart will be also.

"My friends, your Father is the One you should be living for. Do not seek after fame or fortune on this earth, for it will pass away, but your Father will never pass away and neither will His rewards.

"The eye is the lamp of the body; so then if your eye is clear, your whole body will be full of light. But if your eye is bad, your whole body will be full of darkness. If then the light that is in you is darkness, how great is the darkness!"[55]

*It feels like a tornado just swept through my mind, for this message appears contrary to everything that I have been taught.*

136

# CHAPTER SEVENTEEN

Laban interrupts, "Peter, what is this talk of having a clear eye and a bad eye? I do not understand what this has to do with storing up treasure in heaven."

"Jesus was referring to a Jewish expression, which was and still is common among my people. When someone is generous, we say that his eye is clear, but if someone is stingy, we say that his eye is bad, which is a symbol for the worthlessness of such an individual. Jesus was making the point that we are to be generous, and in so doing, we would store up treasure in heaven."

"Peter, I have no treasure stored up anywhere, not on earth or in heaven," Josiah responds.

"The same is true for me," Laban adds.

"It is never too late to be kind, to give selflessly of yourselves, my friends," I answer.

"I shall pray that I would have an opportunity to be generous even in this place, even in the short time I that have left," Josiah responds.

"Peter, how awful it will be for me to meet Jesus for the first time empty handed! I cannot bear the thought," Laban said.

"You will not be empty handed, my friend, for your hands will hold a surrendered heart that loves Him, which is the gift He most desires."

"Oh, if only I had encountered Jesus years ago," Josiah sorrowfully states.

"The important thing is that you know Him now. When Jesus died on the cross, there were two thieves hanging on each side of Him. One mocked Him, but the other asked Jesus to remember him after He died. Jesus responded, 'Today you shall be with Me in Paradise.'

"Laban, that thief had only hours to live, but the Lord welcomed him into Paradise just the same as He does with someone who has served Him for many years. It is never too late to fix your gaze upon the One who thinks you're wonderful," I respond.

"I am so thankful that Jesus is not like men," Laban states.

"As am I," I say.

"Peter, how are your wounds? Are you still in great pain?" Josiah asks.

"My pain is great, but my love is stronger as is my desire to see all of you come to the saving knowledge of Jesus Christ."

"I have been asking Jesus to keep Brutus far from you, my friend," Josiah responds.

"For which I am ever so grateful. Even though I will never betray my Beloved, I still do not relish the thought of suffering.

"Now, let us return to the sermon on the mount. This message is fundamental for every follower of Christ, for it clearly describes how to go about our daily lives. It is not optional and it is not just for the elite; it is for everyone who names the name of Jesus. "

# CHAPTER EIGHTEEN

This was the most powerful, and at the same time, the most bewildering, troubling sermon I had ever heard.

*I wonder if my forefathers felt this same way when Moses gave them the Law?*

Jesus suddenly paused in front of a man who was so busy counting his money that he did not even notice that the Master stood looking at him. Jesus knelt beside him. Obviously nervous, the man quickly picked up his coins and placed them into a leather bag. Eyes darting back and forth, he tucked it under his thigh.

With great kindness, Jesus reached out His hand and gently laid it on the man's shoulder and said, "No one can serve two masters; either he will hate the one and love the other, or he will be devoted to one and despise the other. My friend, you cannot serve God and wealth."

The man quickly looked away; his hand slid under his thigh and clutched his money bag. The Master stood saying, "For this reason I say to you, do not be worried about your life, as to what you will eat or what you will drink; nor for your body, as to what you will wear. Is there not more to life than food, and more to the body than clothing?

"Look at the birds of the air," He said pointing to a small flock of sparrows flying overhead. "They do not sow, nor reap, nor gather into barns and your heavenly Father feeds them. Are you not worth much more than they?"

With a wide sweep of His arm, He continued, "And which one of you by being worried can add a single hour to your life?"

He paused as if waiting for a reply and then continued, "And why are you worried about clothing? Just look at the lilies of the field," He said pointing to a nearby field. "See how beautifully they grow! They do not work neither do they weave cloth, yet I say to you that not even Solomon in all his glory clothed himself as splendidly as one of these. If God so clothes the grass of the field, which is alive today and tomorrow is thrown into the furnace, will He not much more clothe you? Oh, what little trust you have!"

Jesus continued, "Since what I say is true then do not worry, saying, 'What will we eat?' or 'What will we drink?' or 'What will we wear for clothing?' For the Gentiles eagerly seek these things, and your heavenly Father knows that you need all these things. I tell you again not to worry, but instead seek first His Kingdom and His righteousness and all these things will be added to you."

Returning to the man who had resumed counting his money, Jesus said, "So, do not worry about tomorrow; for tomorrow will care for itself. Each day has enough trouble of its own."

The man glanced up, but immediately turned away.

*The Master's words are so foreign. What kind of doctrine is this? Put God's Kingdom first and pursue righteousness and everything I need will be given to me? This is absolutely contrary to all that I know and all that I have been taught.*

Like a man who suddenly remembered something very important, Jesus hurried to the outskirts of the crowd where a group of women stood huddled together. They were obviously harlots. Jesus walked within an arm's reach of them; He stopped and smiled. They each turned away in shame.

"Rightfully so," I said to myself.

He then walked over to a nearby group of men huddled together like a jury deliberating a trial. Stopping directly in front of them, the Master, with great kindness and much authority said, "Do not judge, and you will not be judged. Do not condemn, and you will not be condemned. Pardon, and you will be pardoned. In what way you judge others, that is the way you will be judged; and by whatever standard you use to measure others, that same standard will be used to measure you."

Their expressions revealed the fact that they were offended, yet none dared to look the Master in the eyes. Jesus waited a moment and then returned by way of the harlots. Stopping in front of them, He lifted each woman's chin and quietly spoke to each one, which caused them to weep.

*The crowd is not happy about this.*

Returning to the platform, He laid His hand on my shoulder and said, "A pupil is not above His teacher, is he?"

"Of course not," I answered.

"Everyone, after he has been fully trained, will be like his teacher. So, why do you look at the speck that is in your brother's eye, but do not notice the log that is in your own eye?"

Jumping down He continued, "Or how can you say to your brother, 'Brother, let me take out the speck that is in your eye,' when you do not see the log that is in your own eye? You hypocrite, first take the log out of your own eye, and then you will see clearly to take out the speck that is in your brother's eye.

"Do not give what is holy to dogs, and do not throw your pearls before swine, or they will trample them under their feet and turn and tear you to pieces.

"Give, and it will be given to you; blessings will pour into your lap. As a matter of fact, the blessings will come to you in a good measure—pressed down, shaken together and running over. The standard of measure you use to determine your giving is the same measure that will be used to bless you in return.

"Ask, and it will be given to you; seek, and you will find; knock, and it will be opened to you. For everyone who asks receives, and he who seeks finds, and to him who knocks, it will be opened.

"Or what man is there among you who, when his son asks for a loaf, will give him a stone? Or if he asks for a fish, he will not give him a snake, will he? If you then being evil, know how to give good gifts to your children, how much more will your Father who is in heaven give what is good to those who ask Him!

"In everything and in every way, therefore, treat people the same way you want them to treat you, for this is the Law and the Prophets.

"I know that you believe that Israel as a whole will be saved and that the few among you who would be lost would be exceptions. But, I say to you, enter through the narrow gate; for the gate is wide and the way is broad that leads to destruction, and there are many who enter through it. For the gate is small and the way is narrow that leads to life, and there are few who find it.

"Beware of false prophets who come to you in sheep's clothing, but inwardly are ravenous wolves. You will know them by their fruits, for there is no good tree which produces bad fruit, nor, on the other hand, a bad tree which produces good fruit. For each tree is known by its own fruit.

"Men do not gather figs from thorns, nor do they pick grapes from a briar bush. The good man, out of the good treasure of his heart brings forth what is good; and the evil man out of his evil treasure brings forth what is evil; for his mouth speaks that which fills his heart. So then you will know them by their fruits.

"Not everyone who says to Me, 'Lord, Lord,' will enter the Kingdom of heaven, but he who does the will of My Father who is in heaven will enter. Many will say to Me on that day, 'Lord, Lord, did we not prophesy in Your name, and in Your name cast out demons, and in Your name perform many miracles?' And then I will declare to them, 'I never knew you; depart from Me, you who practice lawlessness.'

"Why do you call me, 'Lord, Lord,' and do not do what I say?

"Everyone who comes to Me and hears My words and acts on them, I will show you whom he is like: he is like a man building a house who dug deep and laid a foundation on the rock. A flood came and the storm burst against that house, but it could not shake it because it had been well-built.

"But the one who has heard and does not act on what he has heard, is like a man who built a house on the ground without any foundation. The torrent burst against that house, and immediately it collapsed; the ruin of that house was great.[56]

"My friends, what I am saying to you today is not optional, this is how your Father's Kingdom operates and this is how everyone of you should live."

The people looked as overwhelmed as I felt. It was obvious that Jesus was presenting the Law, but he did so in a light that was entirely new. He spoke like a Judge presiding over His court. His words were delivered with authority and pierced my heart even though I could not, at that time, fully comprehend the magnitude of what He said.

I thought back to Moses climbing Mount Sinai. He climbed alone because the people were too afraid of God to go themselves. But God, in His great lovingkindness, remembered His people. He came to the earth and wrote the Law with His own finger on two tablets of stone, and the first covenant was given.

*I feel as though that moment in history is being reenacted right before my eyes. Today, like Moses, Jesus ascended a mountain and invited the people to follow Him. This time, unlike the first time, they accepted His invitation and climbed the mountain where God came down and wrote a new covenant on our hearts, not on tablets of stone. In so doing, we heard with our own ears from One who is much greater than Moses. It is the Law, but shone in a brand new light!*

Andrew elbowed me. "What are you smiling about?" he asked.

"I'm not exactly sure. I only know that something very significant happened here today. Something much more significant than we know."

"That may be, but the Master left five minutes ago," Andrew replied.

"I hadn't notice," I responded, jumping off the platform.

Pride flooded my being as I ran after this amazing Rabbi. Oh, how proud I was to be among His disciples, to be His apostle!

# CHAPTER NINETEEN

Josiah interrupts, "Peter, is it enough to just believe that Jesus is the Son of God?"

"Jesus taught that salvation is not based on our deeds, but on what He did for us on the cross. Our deeds can never save us," I answer.

"Then salvation is more than me making a decision to follow Him?" Justus asks.

"The decision to follow Jesus is just the beginning of the journey, my friend. Salvation is very much like being born again. When a baby is born, he is completely dependent upon another to meet his needs. Someone must feed him, clothe him, change him and love him even when it is inconvenient.

"When we surrender our lives to Jesus and accept His forgiveness, we become like a newborn babe. We become completely dependent upon Him to give us life, to change us into His image, to protect, discipline and nurture us, and that is exactly what He does. He feeds us the pure milk of the word and clothes us in His garments of righteousness. He fills us with His love, which transforms us into His image. As we grow, He disciplines us as any good father disciplines his children. And through it all, He loves us unconditionally.

"Jesus' sermon on the mount truly challenged me. From childhood, I had been taught to follow the Law, but in doing so I became quite hardhearted and legalistic. Jesus' words revealed that the Law can save no man, that the blood of bulls and goats can never forgive sins. There is only One who can save, and His name is Jesus!"

Justus suddenly interrupts crying out, "I can wait no longer! I, too, desire to know Jesus as my Lord and Savior. I have sinned greatly and need to be forgiven, cleansed and made new. I need to be born again, to learn to obey, and I need to be loved! Oh, Jesus come and save this poor wretched sinner, for I am lost without You!"

Justus sobs as the tangible presence of God fills our cell. I quietly sing a hymn. After which Justus says, "I have never felt such peace, such joy, so much hope! Oh, how wonderful, how marvelous is my Savior's love!"

I close my weary eyes to rest them for a moment as I silently pray. Waves of pain and fatigue sweep over me like waves wash over the beach.

*Father, I ask You for the grace and strength to stay awake that I might speak of Your great love to these who are lost without You.*

Justus suddenly exclaims, startling me, "What a grand day this is! I am free! I am loved! I feel the love of the Master all over me, inside and out, from top to bottom! Oh how glorious! Oh how marvelous! Oh how wonderful is my Savior's love for me!"

"Justus, you are indeed free! The ones who are truly in prison, who truly suffer, are those who have never experienced the Lord and His glorious presence in their lives. That, my friend, is true suffering. What we are suffering right now is temporal, it will come to an end, but there is a soul, a spirit within every man, woman and child that will live forever either with the Master in eternal glory or with Satan in a pit filled with fire and as dark as this cell," I respond.

Justus and Josiah are lost in worship while I fight to stay awake. I soon lose the battle and drift off to sleep. I dream of a grand and glorious wedding banquet. Jesus stands as the Bridegroom at the head of the table. I am surrounded by beauty and joy and light. Table after table is filled with delicious smelling food. There is music, singing and dancing. I see Justus, Josiah and Laban among the wedding guests. The Best Man walks up to me and introduces Himself as Comforter. He then asks, "Is it well with your soul, My friend?"

I look closely at this Man who looks very much like the Master and reply, "It is very well with my soul, my Friend."

He then lays His hand on my shoulder and says, "You have become as beautiful as the full moon, as pure as the sun, as awesome as a victorious army. You are making it through the wilderness of life leaning on your Beloved.[57] In this place of suffering, you have learned that it is not the strength of your commitment to Jesus that keeps you, but the strength of Jesus' commitment to you that makes you victorious.

"Now come, My friend, for the Master has been longing to see you."

Just as I turn around, a far away voice calls to me saying, "Peter, are you awake? Peter?"

I realize that it is Josiah's voice that is calling to me and fight my way out of my wonderful sleep. I answer, "I was having the most wonderful dream, my friends. A dream about the importance of living this life completely dependent upon the Lord Jesus. I know that I can do nothing without Him and have no desire to even try. And, with the Master to lean upon, I can do anything that He should ask."

Strength from above pours into me and lifting my head, I respond, "I thank God for your desire to know the Master, my friends."

"We let you sleep for as long as we could stand it. It's just that we are well aware of how little time we have left, and the more we learn of this Man, the more we want to know. And, I for one, desire to meet Jesus with a heart filled with love," Josiah states.

"And so you shall. Now let us turn our attention back to this Man who lived in such a way that He turned not only a dozen immature, self-focused disciples upside down, but also the world."

Josiah responds, "Peter, I cannot explain how it happened, but since I gave my life to Jesus, I am different. I think differently and have, for the first time in my life, a desire to do good and to be kind. I am changed, if you know what I mean."

"I know exactly what you mean, for I experienced the power of the Master's love myself," I answer.

Justus adds, "I came into this prison angry and full of hate, but

I no longer feel these things. It is as if I died and I get to start all over again. Peter, I will go to my grave a new man. It feels so wonderful to not be burdened down with sin and guilt and condemnation. I may be chained, but I feel free!"

"This is a brand new day for you, my friend and brother! Even now, the angels in heaven celebrate your new birth before the throne of the King of Glory!"

"Tell us more, Peter! I must know everything. I must know truth, for their is a hunger growing in my heart that only grows more fierce when fed. It is a hunger for more of God," Justus desperately cries out.

# CHAPTER TWENTY

After delivering His profound and challenging sermon, Jesus led the multitude down the mountain. The atmosphere was sober; the crowd was unusually quiet. It goes without saying that there were many who did not understand what the Master said as well as some who disagreed with His words. I was in the first category.

Standing in the valley, surrounded by a sea of people, Jesus announced that we were going to Capernaum.

According to His custom and the custom of all rabbis, Jesus taught as He walked. I loved watching Him. His ways intrigued, challenged, encouraged but also frustrated me. I was frustrated not because of Him or His messages, but because of me and my weakness. I hated weakness and worked diligently to rise above my human frailty. I was quite ambitious and self-centered and following the Master revealed to me just how much I had to learn. My normal mode of operation was no longer acceptable, for the Master had a way of exposing my weaknesses while, at the same time, embracing and encouraging me, which was the way He interacted with everyone He met.

Capernaum was only a two-hour walk from the Mount. As we neared the city, I looked over this little fishing town, which was not only my hometown but also the home of the court official whose child Jesus had healed. It was also the place where the paralytic was let down through the roof and made completely whole. It was to this humble town in which so many miracles had taken place that the Master led us.

As soon as we entered the city gates, the people flocked to the Master making requests and asking questions. Every day, all day long, the demands placed on Jesus were tremendous, but He continued to do only what His Father told Him to do, nothing more and nothing less. I soon learned that it was not their hunger or zeal that caused Him to respond, but His Father alone determined His actions. But this did not hinder the people from crowding around Him; it seemed that everyone wanted something from Him.

I wondered if the Master was aware that many followed Him only because of the signs and wonders that He did. In reality, there were probably only a few who truly drew near to Him because of love. The amazing thing was that Jesus treated both groups alike. He did not show partiality to those who loved Him and neither did He condemn those who selfishly followed. He always spoke the truth in love, showering people with encouragement, drawing and inviting them to come closer while lovingly revealing the hidden things of their hearts. He was indeed the best Shepherd I had ever seen or known or heard of.

We no sooner entered the city gates when several Jewish elders, dressed in their finery, approached. I braced myself for another conflict, but surprisingly it did not come. The eldest among them warmly greeted the Master and then said, "Rabbi, we have been sent by a certain Gentile centurion who is a Roman officer. We can vouch for his character, for he is a good man; he is kind and generous to both Jew and Gentile. This man, though he is a Gentile and a Roman loves Israel and the God of Israel."

The man standing to his right added, "The reason he has sent us to find You is because one of his slaves is very sick. He is paralyzed and fearfully tormented. The slave is esteemed very highly by the centurion and is very dear to him. We have been sent to ask You to come and save his life."

A third man spoke, "Rabbi, the centurion who sent us is worthy of your attention. He loves our nation; it was he, a Gentile, who built our synagogue. Would You come and grant his request?"

*What will He do? Will He go to this Roman?*

Jesus remained motionless as He peered deeply into their eyes.

*This is a wise centurion; he understands that the Romans and Gentiles are despised and hated by the Jewish people; therefore, he sent these Jewish elders. Brilliant strategy, but no self-respecting Jewish man would go help a Roman, but the Master is unlike any other.*

And, just as I suspected, Jesus agreed to go!

*Does He plan to show mercy to this Roman soldier who is Israel's greatest enemy? Are there no limits to the Master's love and compassion?*

Jesus followed the elders out of Capernaum; many followed. We walked along the narrow, rocky road that led to Tiberias, and all the while, the elders did not stop speaking about the centurion. They relayed story after story about the kind deeds and extravagant generosity of this man. It was clear that they held this Roman soldier in high esteem, which was unheard of especially among Jewish leaders.

We had traveled quite a distance when one of the men pointed to a large, but simple stone house on the far side of a nearby field and said, "That is where the centurion lives. He has not only brought the servant into his own house but has made a bed for him near his own room that he might personally attend to his needs."

The man continued, "Come, let us hurry, for we are almost there."

Coming around a bend in the road, we were met by two men running towards us. Greeting us ever so warmly, they quickly turned their attention to the Master. One of them said, "Rabbi, I am Tychius, and this is Anthony. We are friends of the Centurion. He has sent us to tell You not to trouble Yourself any further, for he does not wish to impose upon You. He has asked us to...."

Tychius was suddenly interrupted by a man running towards us through the middle of the field shouting, "Rabbi!"

Jesus took a step in his direction and then stopped.

The man increased his speed; his arms waved wildly. He did not slow his pace until he was within a few feet of the Master. Dropping to his knees on the hard ground, out of breath, he said, "Master, I am not worthy neither morally nor spiritually for You to come under my roof, and it was for this reason that I did not come to You in person."

At this point, Jesus raised him up. The man, now standing before the Master with his head down, continued, "I, too, am a man under authority. I have over one hundred soldiers in my charge. I say to this one, 'Go!' and he goes, and to another, 'Come!' and he comes, and to my slave, 'Do this!' and he does it. I know that You are also a man under authority.

"Oh, kind Master, if You would but say the word my servant will be healed!"

Jesus was visibly moved. He turned to the watching crowd and loudly exclaimed, "Truly I say to you, I have not found such great faith like this with anyone in Israel!"

*Jesus is comparing this Gentile, this Roman soldier to Israel! This cannot be!*

He continued, "I say to you that many will come from the east and from the west and recline at the table with Abraham, Isaac and Jacob in the Kingdom of heaven; but the sons of the Kingdom will be cast out into the outer darkness; in that place there will be weeping and gnashing of teeth."

*Can God reject His chosen people? Would He cast us into hell where the fire never goes out? And would He dare to include Gentiles in that great Sabbath feast that is yet to come when the Messiah will dine with Abraham, Isaac, Jacob and all of Israel? This is impossible, for every Jew knows that no Gentile will have any part in that feast!*

Jesus turned to the centurion and said, "Go your way; it shall be done for you as you have believed."

The centurion, beside himself with joy, embraced the Master, kissing both cheeks. Tears flowed like a river down his face as he thanked Jesus profusely. Jesus threw His arms around the man's neck, and they rejoiced greatly.[58]

# CHAPTER TWENTY-ONE

E leazar grunts loudly, interrupting me and then says, "Peter, are you saying that Jesus healed the centurion's servant without even touching or seeing him?"

"That is exactly what happened. The following day, the Centurion sent a messenger who reported that his servant was healed at the very time Jesus said that he would be well," I answer.

Eleazar interjects, "I have heard a few reports of people being healed, but I have never heard of a miracle that was performed without the person even going to the one who was sick. What you say is impossible, and I do not believe it!"

Laban responds, "Well, I believe it! Peter has no reason to lie to us; he has nothing to gain by telling us this. As a matter of fact, he could be sleeping right now instead of taking the time to answer our questions and telling us about the Master. Can't you see that?"

Eleazar grunts.

"All you do is grunt and complain," Laban replies.

Another grunt.

Ignoring him, Laban turns his attention to me and says, "I would have given anything to have been one of His followers and see His miracles."

I respond, "After Jesus was resurrected from the dead, He said,

'Because you have seen Me, have you believed? Blessed are those who have not seen Me and still believe.'[59]

"You see, Laban, it is not necessary to see Jesus or experience His miracles in order to be one of His followers. It's not too late, my friend; you can still choose to become one of His disciples."

"I am a murderer and a thief, Peter," Laban answers.

"Laban, no one has ever loved sinners as much as Jesus. He came for sinners. No one is too far from His reach, no one is too filthy for Him to cleanse and no one is too evil for Him to redeem. He has proven His love for you by becoming a criminal in your place as He hung on that cross, Laban. The question is not whether He will accept you; the question is will you accept Him? Will you accept His free gift of salvation? A gift that none of us deserve and can never earn."

"What must I do to be saved, Peter?" Laban asks.

"Do you believe that Jesus is the Son of God, Laban?"

"I do indeed," he answers.

"Then give Him your life, give Him your past, your present and your future. Give Him the mess you have made of your life with all its mistakes and wickedness, and He will clothe you in His garments of righteousness in exchange."

"I shall, Peter, I shall!" Laban exclaims.

Without any further encouragement, Laban prays, "Jesus, I give You my life and all that it is. I'm ashamed to say that there isn't much to it, but such as it is, if You want it, it's Yours. Forgive me and cleanse me from all my evil ways. And, Jesus, I accept Your free gift of salvation."

"My friend, the angels in heaven are rejoicing over your confession. You now belong to the King, and you shall live with Jesus for all eternity," I say.

Silence fills our prison.

"Justus, my friend, do you sleep?"

"How could I sleep when you are sharing with us words of eternal life? No, Peter, I am very much awake. I am merely wrestling with my own thoughts."

"And what would those thoughts be?"

"My heart is filled with regret, for I have wasted my life. I have lived a life that amounts to nothing. I feel great sadness over the fact that my life will soon come to an end and I will meet the Master with nothing to offer Him."

"My friend, you will have a surrendered heart to give Him, and that is what He most desires," I answer.

"Oh, how thankful I am that He is loving, compassionate and full of mercy," Justus replies.

"I, too, am thankful that He is so good," Laban adds.

"As am I," I say.

"They will soon come for us, Peter. If you have the strength, would you please tell us more about this wonderful King?" Laban excitedly asks.

"I would be delighted to do so."

# CHAPTER TWENTY-TWO

The morning after Jesus healed the Centurion's servant, we left Capernaum and traveled the twenty-five miles to the small city of Nain. As usual, we were accompanied by a large crowd.

It was nearly evening when we approached the walled city. Rich gardens and fertile fruit trees filled the landscape. Here Jesus stopped as if waiting for something or someone. He did not speak, but merely gazed at the city gate. After some time, I decided to sit. It was then that I heard the distant wailing of mourners and the sound of flutes and timbrels. Jesus stepped out from under the trees and looked toward the sounds.

*Jesus knew that this funeral procession was on its way! That's what He's been waiting for! Amazing!*

The funeral orator led the procession through the gate as he loudly proclaimed the dead man's good deeds. Following him were the hired mourners, women who cried out with loud weeping and wailing. The flute and timbrel players followed behind them. And after them came the dead man, with his face uncovered, laid on a bier made of cedarwood and carried by six barefoot men according to our Jewish customs.

The procession stopped only long enough for the six men to be relieved of their duties by six new ones. During this interval, there was loud lamentation and weeping.

Having completed the exchange, the procession moved forward. Following the bier were the dead man's relatives and friends who were then followed by the general crowd made up of anyone they encountered along the way.

According to Jewish custom, anyone who comes upon a funeral must show his respect to the dead by joining the procession. I looked behind the Master at the large crowd of followers.

*This is going to be the largest funeral procession in all of Israel's history.*

As they passed by, I stepped out to join them, but stopped when I saw that the Master was not moving.

*Why is He not joining them? It is unthinkable and highly insulting for us to not join the procession.*

My thoughts were interrupted by the desperate cries of an elderly woman who was clinging to the bier.

The Master watched the heartbreaking scene intently. Returning to His side, I asked, "Master, we are going to join them are we not?"

Without taking His eyes off of the distraught woman, He replied, His voice cracking, "Her husband is dead and this young man was her only son."

He then looked at me and, with tear-filled eyes, continued, "Peter, this woman is completely alone; she has no one to help care for her."

*We've never seen this woman or her son before. How does He know that her husband is dead and that this dead man is her only son? How does He know that she is completely alone?*

"Come, Peter," Jesus said as He stepped forward. Instead of taking His place at the end of the procession, Jesus walked right up to this woman and laid His hand on the bier. The men carrying it immediately stopped. Within minutes, the mourners stopped wailing and the instruments grew silent. Everyone looked at the Master who had subjected Himself to the greatest of all defilements by touching the bier of a dead man.

Ignoring them, Jesus very tenderly said to the widow, "Do not weep."

*Strange words. Custom dictates that everyone should weep, even strangers.*

The distraught woman looked up into eyes of pure love. A gust of wind caught her black veil and blew it from her head revealing a face etched with more than wrinkles. This was a face that had known deep sorrows and great hardship. Her eyes were bloodshot, and her nose was bright red from much crying. Her cheeks and neck were wet with tears, and her chin quivered.

*From her attire, I would guess that she is quite poor.*

The grieving widow made no response, but merely reached up and with trembling hands, retrieved her veil and covered her head.

Jesus laid His hand on her shoulder. Neither spoke. The woman withdrew ever so slightly, but kept her eyes on the Master. It seemed as though time stood still. The perplexed crowd began to stir; their murmurs sounded like the falling of leaves on a windy day. The Master peered into the eyes of this woman whose tiny frame trembled before His majesty.

Jesus smiled, giving her shoulder a gentle and reassuring squeeze. Then, He turned to face the dead man. With a shout, which startled everyone, myself included, He commanded, "Young man, I say to you, get up!"

Every other voice was instantly silenced as every eye was on, not the dead man, but on Jesus.

Then it happened. A hand moved then a foot. Suddenly, and without warning, the dead man sat straight up and opened his eyes. Like a crowd in which a lion is loosed from its cage, everyone scattered, shrieking and stepping over each other in their haste to get away. Actually, not everyone ran away. There was One who remained with the young man and his speechless mother, and that was the Master. I must admit that I was perfectly content to watch from a distance.

The young man seemed to be a bit confused, which did not surprise me at all. I would imagine that had I died and come back to life, I would be more than just a little confused.

Turning to his mother, he asked, "Why are you staring at me as if you have seen a ghost? And what am I doing on this funeral bier?"

"You were dead, and now you are alive!" his mother exclaimed.

She grabbed his cheeks and squeezed them with so much enthusiasm that his mouth looked like that of a fish. Tears of joy replaced those of sorrow.

*It is amazing to me how the Master can, in a moment, with a simple word, change the course of a person's life!*

Laughing, Jesus took the young man's hand, helped him off the bier and gave him back to his mother.

Slowly and very cautiously the people returned, but not too close. They, like me, were filled with awe and wonder and fear. From the midst of the crowd, a man shouted, "A great Prophet has arisen among us and, in Him, God has come to help His people!"

Another responded, "God has surely visited His people!"[60]

As the widow embraced her son, smothering him with kisses, an elderly man led out in worship, singing:

"God is our refuge and strength, a very
present help in trouble. Therefore we
will not fear, though the earth should
change and though the mountains slip
into the heart of the sea; though its waters
roar and foam, though the mountains quake
at its swelling pride. We will not fear, for
God has surely visited His people!"[61]

The multitude exploded in praise as the flutes and timbrels joined in the great celebration. Jesus looked heavenward and ever so quietly whispered, "Be glorified, Father."

The widow turned from her son and knelt before the Master. Slowly she looked up into His eyes. Neither spoke, but I could see that volumes were being said. Love flowed between them like honey dropping from the honeycomb.

I whispered to Nathanael, "Today, death met Life."

"And Life overcame death," Nathanael replied.[62]

With a nod and a wave, Jesus continued on.

The news of this miracle quickly spread all over Judea and

throughout the surrounding district of Galilee, even as far as the prison where John the baptizer was being held.

# CHAPTER TWENTY-THREE

Hearing the sound of voices in the distance, I stop. As soon as I am satisfied that they are gone, I continue, "Josiah, Justus, Laban, do you remember me telling you about John the baptizer?"

"Yes," they answer.

"Well, John was in prison when this young man came to life. Several of those who witnessed this astonishing miracle hurried to the prison and reported to John what they had seen. John then sent two of his disciples to Jesus. They came asking, 'Are you the expected One, or do we need to look for someone else?'

"To my surprise, Jesus did not answer them. Instead, He turned His attention to those who had diseases, sicknesses and evil spirits and He healed them all. He gave sight to those who were blind, healed the lame and cleansed the lepers.

"At the end of the day, Jesus turned to John's disciples and said, 'Now go and report to John what you have seen and what you have heard. Tell him that the blind receive their sight, the lame walk, the lepers are cleansed, the deaf hear, the dead are raised up and the poor have the gospel preached to them.'

"The men turned to leave and Jesus added, 'And blessed is he who is not offended at Me.'

"I was struck by the things He used to prove that He was indeed the Messiah: healings, miracles, cleansing of lepers and sharing the good news with the poor! Throughout my lifetime, I have always remembered those things and have diligently pursued to walk in the same way as my Master.

"I thought, at the time, that it was a bit strange for John to send his disciples to inquire as to the identity of Jesus. But, one of the greatest stumbling blocks for the Jewish people was the fact that Jesus did not come with the external pomp and power that all Israel expected the Messiah to be surrounded by. Instead, He came as a lowly carpenter's son who walked among the poor and ate with sinners. It was something to behold, my friends."[63]

Justus adds, "If I were John, I would have done the same thing. Perhaps, John didn't send them in order to find out for himself if Jesus was indeed the Messiah. After all, John was the first one to ever make that decree, so he knew better than anyone who Jesus was. Perhaps, he sent them so that they might see for themselves and believe that Jesus was truly the Son of God."

"I agree with you, Justus. John knew beyond a shadow of a doubt that Jesus was the Messiah the first time he saw Him. John also knew that his mission in life was to prepare the way for the Messiah. Knowing that his time was coming to an end, it was important for John to point his disciples to the Master," I answer.

"I suppose his disciples believed after seeing the miracles?" Laban asks.

"They did and so did many others," I answer.

"Shhh, someone's coming," Laban whispers.

We immediately start praying.

I do not pray because I am not ready to leave this earth. On the contrary, I pray because of Eleazar who has yet to believe.

The sounds in the hall are clear; they are dragging a prisoner into a nearby cell. I pray for the poor soul. It is only after I hear the iron door clang shut and the voices of the soldiers fade into the distance that I relax.

Laban quietly says, "Some days I just wish they would go ahead and kill me and get it over with. The waiting is torturous."

"One day it will be over, my friend. And the question for everyone in this cell is this: where will you spend eternity? Will you be free and dwell in glorious Light or will you remain a prisoner in chains, tormented forever?"

"I am so thankful that you are here, Peter. I know it is selfish of me because you have suffered so much, but if you hadn't come, I would not know the Truth," Laban answers.

"Nor would I," Justus adds.

"Me either," Josiah says.

Eleazar responds rather sarcastically, "Because of you, I get food and water. So, I guess you could say that I am grateful for you as well even if your stories bore me to death."

Ignoring him, Justus says, "Peter, tell us more. Tell us so much that we have no choice but to remain true should we be faced with the dilemma of denying Jesus or living. Convince us that the Master is as lovely as you describe Him to be. Oh, that our hearts would be compelled to make the right choices even if it means our death, just as you have done!"

"A man in love does extravagant things, my friends," I say.

# CHAPTER TWENTY-FOUR

John the baptizer's disciples left. Jesus turned to the crowd and said, "What did you go out to the wilderness to see? A reed shaken by the wind?

"No? But what did you go out to see? A man dressed in soft clothing? Those who wear soft clothing are in kings' palaces! But what did you go out to see? A prophet? Yes, I tell you, and one who is more than a prophet.

"John is the one about whom it was written, 'Behold, I send My messenger ahead of You; he will prepare Your way before You.'[64]

"Truly, I say to you, among those born of women there has not arisen anyone greater than John."

The Master paused as He looked from one face to another. It was easy to guess what the crowd was thinking, for I, too, found myself slightly offended by His statement.

*John the baptizer is greater than our father Abraham? And what about David, Elijah and the other prophets? John did no miracles, he ruled no kingdom; he fathered nothing. He merely preached and baptized. The rough skin of camels was his clothing and locusts and wild honey was his food. He was a man of no reputation, and yet Jesus is saying that John is greater than any man who has ever been born! Impossible!*

*I could not reconcile His statement with my reality, and yet I had never known the Master to say anything that was untrue. If what He says is true, then what standard does the Master use to determine greatness? It is certainly no standard that I am familiar with.*

I turned my attention back to the Master who had resumed speaking, "From the days of John the Baptist until now the Kingdom of heaven suffers violence and violent men take it by force. All the Prophets and the Law prophesied until John, and if you are willing to believe what I am saying, John himself is Elijah who was to come."

Jesus paused again as He scanned the sea of faces.

*John is Elijah! What is He saying? Elijah is suppose to come before the Messiah—but John the baptist is Elijah? How could this possibly be? Perhaps He is speaking in parables?*

Jesus looked directly at me and said, "He who has ears to hear, let him hear."

I looked away. The Master continued, "To what shall I compare this generation?"

Pointing to a group of young children playing nearby, He continued, "This generation is like children sitting in the market place who call out to the other children and say, 'We played the flute for you, and you did not dance; we sang a funeral song for you, and you did not mourn.'

"John came neither eating nor drinking, and they say that he has a demon! The Son of Man came eating and drinking, and they say, 'Behold, a gluttonous man and a drunkard, a friend of tax collectors and sinners.'

"Yet wisdom is vindicated by her deeds. John will be vindicated one day. Rest assured there is a day coming when everything will be made clear."[65]

Putting His arm around James' shoulder, Jesus walked a short distance away and stopped. Turning around, He surveyed the vast crowd made up of people from many different cities. Releasing James from His embrace, He shouted, "Woe to you, Chorazin! Woe to you, Bethsaida! For if the miracles had occurred in Tyre and Sidon which occurred in you, they would have repented long ago in sackcloth and ashes. Nevertheless, I say to you, it will be more tolerable for Tyre and Sidon in the day of judgment than for you!

"And you, Capernaum, do you think you will be lifted up to heaven? You will be thrown down to Hades! Many miracles have been done in you. If these same miracles had occurred in Sodom, that city would still be standing this day. Nevertheless, I say to you that it will be more tolerable for the land of Sodom in the day of judgment, than for you."

Lifting His eyes to heaven, He prayed, "Father, Lord of heaven and earth, I praise You because You have hidden these teachings from the wise and intelligent. I thank You that You have revealed them to infants. Yes, Father, for this way was well-pleasing in Your sight."

Turning His eyes back to the multitude, He said, "My Father has given Me all things! Only the Father knows who the Son is. And only the Son knows who the Father is. And the only people who will know about the Father are those people whom the Son chooses to tell."

Jesus pointed to an elderly man a short distance away who was struggling under the weight of a large bag of seed and said, "You are tired and carry heavy loads. If all of you will come to Me, I will give you rest. Take My yoke upon you and learn of Me, for the yoke I give you is easy, and My burden is light.

"Take only the responsibilities that I give to you, not those put on you by man or by religious traditions. Find out who I am; learn what My nature and character is like, for I am gentle and humble in heart. Discover who I am, and you will find rest for your souls."[66]

With a nod, He ran to the man struggling under the weight of his load. After speaking with him, Jesus lifted the bag from his shoulder and placed it across His own. The grateful and surprised man straightened up, wiping the sweat from his face and neck.

Jesus carried the bag to the man's cart while the people and tax collectors discussed the Master's words. I looked around at the crowd. I had come to know many of them. I found it interesting that those who were baptized with John's baptism found it easier to receive the Master's teaching than those who were not baptized by John, including the Pharisees and Scribes. Those who rejected the Master's words rejected God's purposes for their lives.

*Oh, how dangerous it is to think so highly of yourself and your opinions that you cannot hear truth when it is so clearly presented and even confirmed with miracles and signs.*

I watched as the Pharisees and lawyers walked away, their heads held high and their hearts tightly closed.

# CHAPTER TWENTY-FIVE

Our prison door slowly opens, and relief floods my being as Malchus whispers, "Do not be afraid; I have brought food and water."

Placing his dimly lit torch in the holder, he quickly closes the door. "Malchus, my faithful brother, greetings in the name of the Lord."

Holding the wonderful water to my parched lips, I drink deeply as Malchus asks, "How are your wounds, my friend?"

"Thanks to your medicine and the prayers, I am feeling very little pain," I answer then take another very long drink of water, which helps to soothe my dry, parched mouth and throat.

"I am so glad to hear that, Peter," he says as he places a piece of goat cheese in my mouth. "But, I am afraid that I have come with sad news."

"Do not waste another moment. Pray tell me is it news of my wife that you bring?"

"No, my friend, it is not. The news is about our brother, Tiberias. Yesterday, he was executed and is now with the Master."

"How precious in the sight of the Lord is the death of His saints," I whisper to myself.[67]

"Peter, I was present at his execution. You would have been so proud of him. As he was led across the arena, he boldly proclaimed the gospel. His strength was remarkable considering the fact that he had been so severely beaten. Among the guards was Asher, the man who betrayed him. As Tiberias was led past Asher, he cried out, 'Asher, my friend, I have forgiven you, and Jesus loves you!'

"Asher turned his face away and moments later the lions were released. But, just before they pounced, Tiberias looked up to heaven and shouted, 'I love You, Jesus!' His face literally shone, and he was filled with great joy. It was incredible to see causing me and several others to weep.

"I looked over at Asher who was now on his knees in agony. Stepping closer, I heard him crying out for God to have mercy on his soul and was asking Jesus to forgive him! The guards quickly took him to the Centurion who had Asher thrown into the cell next to yours. I am going to see him when I leave you."

I reply, "My soul rejoices that Asher has repented and turned his soul over to a faithful, compassionate and forgiving King. And I greatly rejoice that our friend and brother, Tiberias, has obtained as a result of his faith the salvation of his soul![68]

"Malchus, are we not rich men because the Master died and rose again? We are forgiven because He was betrayed! We are free because He became a criminal! The Master grows more beautiful the closer I get to Him, which is so unlike the things of this earth. Have you not noticed that the closer you look at the things of this earth the more flaws you see? But that is not so with Jesus. He is absolutely perfect and only grows more lovely with each passing day! His love is greater than the deepest ocean, and His mercy is new every morning. I long for the day when I will be reunited with my King. I can hardly wait for that day!"

"Amazing love!" Malchus adds.

"Would you give Asher a message for me?" I ask.

"Certainly."

"Say to him, 'What credit is there for you if you patiently endure being harshly treated when you deserve it? But, if you patiently endure suffering because you have done what is right, you find favor with God. For you have been called for this purpose, since Christ also suffered for you. He left us an example of suffering that we might follow in His steps. Be of good cheer, for your name is written in the Lamb's book of life! Hold fast what you have, and do not let anyone take it from you!'

"Would you also tell him that I will pray for his soul to remain true to the Lord unto the end?"

Justus adds, "Will you tell him that I will pray for him as well?"

"And me too," Laban adds.

"As will I," Josiah says.

"I will tell him," Malchus answers. He then quickly makes his way to each man, Eleazar included, feeding them cheese and water.

"Malchus," I whisper, "have you been able to locate my wife?"

"I have tried, but my inquiries have been blocked at every turn. But, I shall not give up until I know where she is, my friend."

"Thank you," I respond as a deep sadness floods my being.

*I miss her. I miss the sound of her voice, the sparkle in her eye, the strength of her spirit. I miss her touch and her great love for the Lord. She is a beautiful lady who loves the Lord with all of her heart. She has been the perfect companion for me.*

"Peter, I must go now, I dare not remain any longer," Malchus states. With a whispered prayer, he leaves as quickly and silently as he came.

"I cannot understand why Malchus risks his life to help men who are going to die soon," Eleazar says.

I answer, "He does what he does because he loves Jesus and he loves others. You see, my friend, Jesus did the same thing. While we were yet sinners, He died for us. He did not wait for mankind to turn to Him before He died on that cross.

"The love of the Father fills Malchus to the point that he loves his life not unto death. He, too, is a brand plucked from the fire. Malchus does not fear man who can merely kill his body. He fears the One who can deliver his soul to death. Malchus understands that love is more than a word, he understands that following the Master means picking up your cross and following in His steps. Sacrifice, my friend, is a part of loving."

"I would do the same if I were free," Laban answers.

"You need not be free in order to love, my friend. I watched as Jesus continually and without fail made it His policy to love in every situation. He even loved those who persecuted Him, those who did not believe in Him and those who were His enemies. To live this way is true freedom my fellow prisoners in Christ."

"I do not understand how it is possible to love those who are cruel to you. I have not even loved those who were kind to me; instead, I despitefully used them," Laban responds.

"There is One who is able to love like that and He now lives within you. Draw upon His strength and His love. Pray for your enemies, and by the grace that God gives, you will find yourself able to love even those who torture you. That is the nature of prayer, my friends. You will discover that whomever you spend your time praying for soon finds their way into your heart, and before you realize it, you find yourself loving him or her."

"That would be a miracle, Peter. I have spent my life hating those who hurt me and have spent a lot of time and energy finding ways to cause them pain and suffering," Laban answers.

"Jesus said that His followers were to never pay back evil for evil to anyone. He said that we were never to take our own revenge, but to leave room for the wrath of God.

"If your enemy is hungry, feed him, and if he is thirsty, give him a drink, for in so doing you will heap burning coals upon his head. Do not be overcome with evil, but overcome evil with good. That is how I have tried to live my life. I must confess that I have not always lived this way, but I have worked towards that goal. I have learned that one must hate what God hates and love what God loves, for this is the way Jesus lived. We must contend for the fullness of all that God has for us."[69]

"The only thing I am contending for is some sleep. How 'bout being quiet for a while?" Eleazar gruffly asks.

"How can I remain silent when you do not yet know Jesus as your Lord and Savior?"

"When are you going to realize that I am not some weak soul in need of your help?" he replies.

"The real question is when will you realize that you are eternally lost, doomed to spend eternity separated from God, in a pit of fire where you will be constantly tormented? You are much more needy than you know, my friend. There is only One who can help you, but He will certainly reject you if you deny Him access to your life."

"Like I said, could you shut up and let me get some sleep?"

"Peter, Eleazar may not want to hear, but we do. Please continue on," Josiah says.

"So I shall for your sakes and for Eleazar."

## CHAPTER TWENTY-SIX

All of the Pharisees left except one and he waited until the others had disappeared from sight before he invited the Master to dine at his house. I was neither shocked nor surprised when Jesus accepted. As we walked along, the Pharisee introduced himself as Simon, the son of Cyrus. He spent the entire time bragging about his achievements, his status in society and the enormous wealth he had accrued. Jesus listened quietly and much more patiently than I would have, but it was obvious to me that He was not impressed and neither was I.

*Simon hasn't invited Jesus to his house because of His teachings. It appears to me that he is merely following protocol, which obliges the leading Pharisee of a city to host a distinguished rabbi. It also gives him the perfect opportunity to talk about himself.*

We soon arrived at the Pharisee's house, which, from the way he had talked, I would have thought to be much more grand than it was.

Simon ushered us directly into the dining hall.

*How rude of him to not have his servants wash our feet! He didn't even offer us the water so that we could wash ourselves!*

Simon motions for us to take our places at the table.

Ignoring this insult, the Master reclined at this man's table. Within minutes, several other Pharisees made their grand appearance. They were dressed in the finest of fabrics with all their tassels and bells and fringes. They paraded across the room like royalty and took their places front and center as usual.

I looked down at my thread bare garment and must admit that I was quite uncomfortable. The servants were dressed in clothes much nicer than anything I had ever worn. They rushed here and there in response to their master's every command.

I looked at Jesus hoping that He would leave, but, having come to know Him, I was very doubtful that He would. To my dismay, Jesus was not even looking at these puffed up Pharisees. Instead, He was staring in the direction of the servants' entrance.

The doorway was empty, and no one stood near it.

*Is He watching for someone, or is He merely trying to ignore the arrogance of his host and his guests?*

I quickly turned my eyes back to the Master, hoping to get His attention, but His gaze remained fixed. Suddenly, a faint glimmer of light filled His eyes, and His expression softened.

I looked at the object of His attention and saw, standing in the doorway, a woman known in the city as a harlot. Her face was painted with the brightly colored cosmetics worn by those of her kind. Her long, black hair hung freely over her mostly bare shoulders; she wore no veil as was the manner of harlots.

*How did this harlot gain entry to this house?*

I looked at Simon. His face was red.

*Is he angry or embarrassed?*

Simon was squirming in his seat.

*Perhaps the servants allowed her entrance because she has been here before? Or perhaps she knows one of the servants? I suppose it matters little how she gained entrance. The real question is why has she come? For what purpose?*

Simon loudly cleared his throat. I looked back at the object of his agitation. The harlot, with head bent low and eyes on the floor, was slowly making her way towards Jesus. Her shadow fell on us all, but she said not a word. Stopping just behind the Teacher's feet in the manner of a servant, she ever so briefly glanced up. Tears ran down her face, washing away the shameful paint.

No one spoke, and no one moved. Every eye was fixed on this woman and the Master.

*What is she going to do? What is He going to do? And what need could she have that would make her desperate enough to risk humiliation and rejection by coming here?*

She lifted her trembling hand from the folds of her garment. I leaned forward to see what she was gripping so tightly. It was only after she fell to her knees that I saw the vial of perfume in her hand.

This woman buried her face on the Master's feet and wept loudly.

Simon again cleared his throat.

She sat up. Her tears were washing away the dust and dirt that had covered Jesus' feet. Before I had decided how I was going to respond to her obnoxious, brazen behavior, she began to dry His feet with her hair!

*Just who does this woman think she is?*

I exploded from my place like an arrow shot from a bow. For the first time since this woman appeared, the Master looked away and looked directly at me. There was a fire in His eyes that I had never seen before; it caused my insides to tremble. I sank back to the floor afraid to move. And all the while, this woman washed His feet with her tears and dried them with her hair.

To my horror, she rested her cheek against the Master's feet. Her tears had finally stopped and the Master's had begun.

The harlot covered His feet with kisses—defiling, disgusting kisses! I looked at James and John. They were just as disgusted as I. Judas looked on with great interest. Matthew and John's face showed great compassion and much tenderness. Andrew looked puzzled.

*How can Jesus endure this? Surely He knows who she is and what she does! I do not understand His response at all!*

And then, as if that was not enough, the woman took the vial of perfume, which she still clutched in her trembling hand and poured it on His feet. Within minutes, the sweet fragrance filled the entire room. Undaunted by her disapproving audience, the harlot rubbed the fragrant ointment over His feet and ankles.

*This is unlawful! This is too much!*

I looked at the Master's face. His eyes were closed as if to block out any distraction. Tears glistened on His eyelashes.

*He not only permits her to touch Him, but He is deeply moved by her affection! I do not understand this!*

Suddenly, I remembered Jesus' words about being a Physician who seeks out those in need. I took a deep breath and looked closely at the harlot.

*She weeps like one who has found something that is very precious and fears that she will lose it again.*

Her tears began again.

*Only a truly repentant heart dares to risk such a potentially humiliating situation as this.*

The vial, which held the expensive perfume, now laid on the floor completely empty, but its fragrance was being enjoyed by all.

*This woman certainly has paid a high price in coming here, not just with her pride, but also with the perfume. She certainly appears to be sincere, but what a shame, what a waste that she is a harlot!*

The Master cleared His throat and said, "Simon, I have something to say to you."

Thinking Jesus was addressing me, I slowly lifted my eyes. To my relief, He was speaking to our inconsiderate host. He and the other Pharisees present were so bloated by their self-righteous pride that I feared they would burst like an old wine skin that has been filled with new wine.

Simon looked up and, in accordance with the fake politeness of many Pharisees, responded, "Say it, Teacher."

Jesus said, "There were two men. Both men owed money to the same moneylender. One man owed him five million silver coins, and the other man owed him five hundred. Neither of them could pay their debt. So, the moneylender forgave them both, erasing their debts from his books. Now Simon, which of them, do you suppose, will love the moneylender more?"

Simon's face suddenly looked pained, he shifted in his place, hesitating. He obviously struggled with his answer. Jesus continued to stare directly at him until Simon finally responded, "I suppose that it would be—."

"Yes?" He asked not letting him off the hook.

"Well, perhaps it would be the one who owed him the most money."

"You have answered correctly, Simon."

He then looked down at the woman whose cheek rested on His feet and said, "Simon, do you see this woman?"

Simon reluctantly nodded and answered "Of course I see her. She has made a brazen fool of herself!"

Jesus continued, "Simon, when I came into your house, you provided Me with no water for My feet, which a polite host always does for his guests. But this woman has washed My feet with her tears and has dried them with the only thing she had—her hair.

"Simon, you did not so much as kiss My cheek, which is the normal greeting of a good host, but this woman has not only kissed My feet, but has smothered them with her kisses!

"You did not rub My head with oil, but she has poured out the entire contents of her vial of precious and valuable perfume on My feet and then lovingly spread it with her very own hands.

"Simon, because of her love for Me, I say to you that her sins, which are many, have been forgiven."

At this point, everyone in the room gasped, myself included.

Undaunted, Jesus continued, "The person who feels only a little need to be forgiven will feel only a little love when forgiven. In like manner, the person who feels a great need to be forgiven will feel a great love when forgiven."

Jesus turned to the harlot and gently said, "Woman."

She slowly looked up. Her dark brown eyes were swimming in a pool of tears. It may sound strange, but this woman somehow looked different to me. It was true that her cosmetics had all been washed away, and she now appeared in her natural state, but there was something else about her. There was something about her eyes, something innocent and pure, something that was not there before. I had no idea what it was, but it was real; it was very real.

Filled with compassion Jesus said, "Woman, your sins are forgiven."

She gasped, clutching her hands over her mouth. A new river of tears spilled down her face.

I heard the murmuring of the Pharisees, "Just who does He think He is? How can He forgive sins? Only God can forgive sins!"

Jesus suddenly sat upright facing this woman. He laid His hand on her bare shoulder and said, "Your faith has saved you; go in peace."[70]

*What kind of love is this? This love that Jesus demonstrates is truly amazing—a love that I have seen in none other! And now, look at this woman! See how she falls on her face weeping even more than before. Look at the love she pours out! She understands something that I do not. She is experiencing something greater than life, something that I have never known. In her fearful state, she has found security. In her desperation, she has found satisfaction. In her turmoil, she has found perfect peace. She has found Life!*

# CHAPTER TWENTY-SEVEN

L aban says, "Peter, I can certainly understand how that woman felt. I have lived a life of sin and debauchery, and to think that Jesus would accept me and forgive me even at this late date is very difficult to believe."

"I understand how you feel, for I, too, am wrestling with feelings of unworthiness and doubts as to whether or not Jesus will truly welcome me into eternity," Justus adds.

"As do I," Josiah says.

"We have all sinned and fallen short of the glory of God. There has only been One who has ever lived a perfect life and—."

Hearing the sound of guards, I stop speaking and pray. The door is thrown open, and a blinding torch is thrust into our cell. Like a flock of vultures, the guards rush in. One guard kicks me while two others unlock my chains. Grabbing the chain around my wrists, they drag me out of the cell and down the long corridor. The rough stones cut into the skin on my backside. I fight to stay conscious, praying continually.

Thankfully, my journey is short. I am dropped on the rough stone floor. Before I can catch my breath, a guard delivers a hard blow to my rib cage ordering me to roll over. Afraid of inciting his anger further, I force my stiff and painful body to comply. Looking up into the eyes of my tormentor, I see the emptiness within, the hopelessness and the pain. I feel great compassion for him, for he is more of a prisoner than I. I have hope, but he has none without Jesus.

A low, guttural sound like that of an angry predator escapes from his throat. "What are you staring at?" he asks.

"I am looking at a man who is greatly loved by his Creator," I answer.

A second guard places his sandaled foot on my chest. It feels as though my ribs will break as I try to inhale. I remind myself that the Master is the only One who can take my life; no man has that power. God alone holds my life in His hands.

*Lord, if my time is over on this earth, if I have brought Your message to all that You have appointed, then I am ready to leave this world, but if there is yet more that I am to do, then I ask You to deliver me from these evil men. Let Your will be done, for I am Yours and Your desire is for me.*[71]

The guard presses more weight on my chest; I hear several ribs crack. My world suddenly goes dark.

I open my eyes only to discover that I am still alive. A deep sadness sweeps over me like a blistering wind blows through the desert.

*Oh, how I long to leave this world behind and step into my eternal home where I will united forever with the Prince of peace and the God of all comfort! Oh, that I might see my beloved King again!*

Excruciating pain floods my being consuming any desire to live.

*Father, grant that Your servant might quickly complete the race that I have been called to run.*

The guard now kneels beside me and my heart is filled with compassion and love for him. With clenched teeth, he asks, "How can you look at me with kindness? Where is the hate?"

With much effort I manage to respond, "Why should I hate you? Hate destroys and creates suffering. I have no desire to see you destroyed or suffering."

"You're right about that! Hate certainly does destroy; I am living proof of that!"

I respond, "What right do I have to hate someone who my Master loves? I choose to love what He loves and hate only what He hates, which is sin.[72] No, my friend, I do not hate you. I rejoice, for today I am counted worthy to suffer for the sake of my Lord!"[73]

Spewing out a string of curse words, he stands and is quickly joined by the other guard. They pick me up and carry me to a door, which another guard kicks opens. I am thrown out. I hear the slamming of the door behind me as I tumble head over heels. When I finally come to a stop, I realize that I am outside. Blinded by the light, I press my face into what feels and tastes like dirt and pray for the strength to remain true to the Master regardless of what should come. I lay in a heap as a dead man and quietly sing:

"The Lord is my light and my salvation;
  whom shall I fear?
The Lord is the defense of my life;
  whom shall I dread?
When adversaries and enemies
  come upon me to devour my flesh,
  they stumbled and fell.
Though a host encamp against me,
  my heart will not fear;
Though war arise against me,
  in spite of this I shall be confident."[74]

Suddenly, wild cheering fills the air. Squinting, I lift my head enough to see that I am in an outdoor arena. I brace myself for what will probably be the end of my natural life and the beginning of eternal bliss. I wait for the pain that is sure to follow, but strangely, nothing happens. The crowd quickly becomes angry and screams for me to get up and fight. I have no idea who or what I am suppose to fight, but it matters not because I am physically unable to get up, much less fight anything.

I keep my face buried in the dirt and tucked under my arm in an effort to protect my eyes from the painful light of day and from whatever torture awaits me.

*Lord, more than anything else, I want to know You intimately and please You completely.*

Something brushes against my arm; cold chills run down my spine. I lift my face just enough to see that a very large lion is sniffing me. The lion suddenly throws his head back and roars!

Needless to say, I am filled with great fear and quickly say outloud, "My heart will not fear, for You, O Lord, are my light and my salvation!"

I brace myself for what is sure to come, but nothing happens. With my head tucked under my arm, I thank God for being in charge of my life.

After a few moments, hearing the ever-increasing anger of the crowd, I dare to look up. I cannot believe my eyes—the lion saunters to the center of the arena where he lies down. The crowd is enraged. They are shouting and cursing and throwing all kinds of objects at the lion in an effort to anger him.

The door behind me opens, and I am suddenly and viciously assaulted from head to toe with rods. "The Lord is the defense of my life," I cry out just before I am rendered unconscious.

Aware of only one thing and that is blinding pain, I wake. I try to move my legs, but find to do so is unbearable.

"Peter, are you okay?" a familiar voice asks.

I try to focus on the voice, to identify it, but cannot. My mind cannot focus; the pain is just too great. I try to speak, but find that I cannot remember how. I groan in an effort to communicate that I am still alive.

"Peter, it's Justus. We've been praying for you. The Lord will raise you up, my friend. He will...." His voice fades into the darkness as I drift away to a place where there is no pain.

I do not know how long I am in that condition. I only know that I am glad to wake and find that my senses are intact and my ability to think clearly has returned. I can hear my friends praying for me.

"Thank you for praying," I manage to choke out.

"Peter, then you are okay?" Justus asks.

"I will be," I answer.

A cry of thanksgiving is offered to Jesus by my fellow prisoners.

My body hurts from head to toe; my leg is certainly broken as are several ribs. But, to my delight, I discover that I am no longer in chains.

*The guards must have thought that I would die, so they did not bother chaining me. How wonderful!*

Eager to be near my friends, I try crawling, but quickly realize that the pain is too great. So, I sing instead. After all, worship is the best medicine.

> "I love Thee, O Lord, my strength.
> The Lord is my rock and my fortress
>     and my deliverer.
> My God, my rock, in whom I take refuge;
> My shield and the horn of my salvation,
>     my stronghold.
> I call upon the Lord, who is worthy to be praised,
>     and I am saved from my enemies.
> The cords of death encompassed me,
>     and the torrents of ungodliness terrified me,
> The cords of Sheol surrounded me;
> The snares of death confronted me.
> In my distress I called upon the Lord,
>     and cried to my God for help;
>     and He heard my voice out of His temple."[75]

I sing until I can sing no more. Exhausted from the relentless pain, I soon fall asleep and dream of Jesus. He is dressed in a shepherd's robe and carries a rod and staff. I cringe at the sight of the rod. He slowly approaches saying, "I am the good Shepherd; I lay down My life for the sheep. Those who trust in Me will never die!" He then leans His rod and staff against a tree. Walking a short distance away, He picks up a frightened lamb whose legs are broken. Carefully and ever so gently placing the little one across His shoulders, He looks up at me and says,

"A bruised reed I will not break."

I wake with a deep ache in my heart. I so long to be with my beloved King. He loves me; He cares. He may not be with me physically, but He resides within. He is my strength and my song. He is the reason I live, and He is worth it all!

My friends are quiet. They must be asleep. I worship and pray until I fall asleep.

The next time I wake, my teeth are chattering from the cold. Justus is praying, which is music to my ears. I lay, unmoving, just listening. Tears quickly fill my eyes. I feel so alone, so painfully alone. I silently cry out, "Lord, I can't make it without You!"

Out of the darkness comes His still, soft voice whispering, "I will stay with you forever! I will never let you go."

Oh, how sweet His voice is!

"Lord, I don't know what tomorrow may bring, but I know that I can trust Your faithfulness. I don't know how much time I have left, but in the end I know that You will be faithful! No matter what may come, I know that You are with me!

"Lord, You surround me! You are beside me! Arm in arm, we walk through this life together. My whole reason for living is found in You! I can't live my life without You!" I cry.

"I will never leave you, My friend," He says as His presence covers me like a warm blanket.

I lay in silence enjoying the respite from the pain that His presence brings.

"Peter?" Justus quietly calls out.

"Yes?"

"Thank God that you are alive!" he replies.

I try sitting up, but find that it is still too painful. Determined to be near my friends, I half drag, half pull myself through the thick darkness, the human waste and the numerous insects. As I am making the slow, arduous journey, Eleazar says, "Peter, how can you remain true to a God who subjects His followers to such awful treatment, to such atrocities as you have endured in the name of your God?"

"I do not base my evaluation of God on the way I am treated at the hands of man. Neither do I—."

Eleazar interrupts, "I am guilty of a crime. I deserve to be in prison, but it seems to me that the only thing you are guilty of is believing in a God who appears to be either extremely cruel or extremely calloused or maybe both."

"Eleazar, the evil that is done to me is not by God's hands. He is a good God; it is only at the hand of evil that such atrocities exist."

Eleazar grunts loudly and curses.

To which I respond, "My brother, persecution causes either growth or bitterness. My response to it determines whether I grow more like my Master or whether I become more like this world and its evil prince, Satan.

"I decided a long time ago that I would not allow myself to become offended with my Lord regardless of my circumstances. You see, Eleazar, I know Jesus in a personal, intimate way. He is not only my Savior, but He is also my dearest and best friend. I talk with Him and He talks with me. Eleazar, Jesus is the kindest, most loving Shepherd you will ever meet!

"He has never forsaken me, neither has He ever left me. He is here, right now, listening to our every word, recording our every thought, and He is watching over us. His presence brings me great comfort.

"It may seem to you that Nero determines our destiny, but he does not have any power over us other than what God gives him. God holds his heart in His hand and He turns him whichever way He wants. No, Nero does not determine my destiny; God alone does that. And when the hour comes for my departure, then I will die, but it will be in God's timing not men's. God will determine when I leave this body of sin and death. In the twinkling of an eye, I will wake up in the presence of my beloved King, and I will be swept into such love, such peace, such kindness and such beauty that nothing else will matter. Jesus Himself will wipe away every tear as He welcomes me into His eternal dwelling place.

"So, my friend and brother, do not think that God is weak or cruel or callous. He merely has a plan for my life, and it is a good plan, a plan to make me into the image of His dear Son."

Eleazar again responds by grunting and cursing.

Justus says, "Peter, when the guards brought you back, they were in an uproar. We could hear them arguing in the hallway. They said that you were thrown into the arena with four lions, but none of the lions would come near you.

"Because the lions would not attack you, Nero commanded the guards to beat you to death. The two guards sent to do so were attacked and killed by the lions. You were alone out there with the lions. Malchus, who was watching and praying just inside the door, ran out and dragged you inside. When the guards brought you here Malchus took off your chains and prayed for you. The other guards watched, and no one stopped him."

"Malchus, my dear brother." I whisper to myself knowing that his actions on my behalf have sealed his fate.

"Peter, I don't mean this disrespectfully, but I must ask the same question Eleazar asked. Why does God allow His faithful servants like you to be so horribly treated?" Justus asks.

"I was wondering the same thing, but was afraid to ask," Laban adds.

"Me, too," Josiah states.

Having finally arrived at Josiah's side, I stretched out my hand and touched my friend's shoulder. "My dear friends, God uses the things Satan means for evil; He turns them into good for us in the end. He uses persecution and suffering and hardships to purify and strengthen our hearts making us like pure gold. Having gone through the fire, we fear nothing.

"Do not think that I am surprised at the fiery ordeal that comes my way; it is for my testing. It is not a strange thing that we will suffer in this life. Did not my Lord suffer greater things than this? If God's very own Son suffered at the hands of men, then should we not expect the same? Why should we be exempt? We are not better than the Son of God, are we? God forbid that we should think so!

"My friends, to the degree that I share in the sufferings of Christ, I will be glad so that when Jesus is revealed in all His glory, I may truly rejoice.

"If I am reviled for the name of Christ, I am a blessed and happy man because the Spirit of glory and of God rests upon me."[76]

Eleazar interrupts saying, "You are a strange man, Peter. I cannot understand your willingness to suffer for your religion. It seems foolish and stupid to me. Why not renounce your faith and go free? Once you are out of this God-forsaken place then you can return to this Jesus, and no one will be the wiser."

"Oh, Eleazar it is obvious that you do not understand the debt of love I owe to the Master. Could you deny your brother or your father? I do not think that you could. So, how could I ever deny One who is closer to me than my brother or father?

"The measure of love is in how much it is willing to suffer, my friend. If one loves only a little, then there will not be that willingness to sacrifice or endure discomfort.

"My love for the Master runs deep because His love for me is endless; therefore, I am willing to suffer whatever should come my way," I respond.

The sound of fast approaching footsteps bring an end to our conversation. I quickly move away, ignoring the horrific pain in my body. Pressing my face against the stone floor, I pray. I can hear my friends praying, with the exception of Eleazar.

*There is no greater joy than knowing those you love are walking with the Lord. Father, grant that Eleazar might come to know Your resurrection power before it is too late.*

The key turns in the lock. With not so much as a glance inside, a guard roughly places a bowl of food and a small bucket of water just inside the door then quickly slams it shut.

Ignoring the pain, I drag my battered body across the stones in an effort to get to the food before the rodents discover it. I thank God that I am not in chains. In the past, the guards occasionally left us food, but we were never able to get to it. We soon learned this was another form of torture. But, this time, thanks to my freedom, we will be the ones who feast and not the rodents.

Scooping the bowl up, I whisper, "Dinner has arrived, my friends!"

Smelling the contents, I add, "It appears to be some form of lentils!"

I am barely able to crawl. How will I ever get this food and water across the room without spilling it? The bucket of water is nearly full, and every drop is precious as is every bite of food.

Since the food bowl is only half full, I pour some of the water into the bowl with the lentils and stir it with the only thing I have available, my dirty hand. Satisfied that I have done all I can to preserve both water and beans, I place the bowl and bucket ahead of me and then drag my broken and very painful leg behind me. I repeat this long and arduous process until I reach Justus.

As I hand-feed him, a rodent runs up my leg. I knock him off saying, "Sorry, fella, you're not invited to this meal."

Once he has eaten and drank, I crawl to Josiah, but he drinks only enough to wet his mouth.

"Have more, my friend, there is plenty," I say pressing the bucket closer. Drawing back, he quietly responds, "I would rather my friends have my share."

I scoop a handful of the lentils. Just as I bring them close to his mouth, he turns his head away. I lower my hand at which point he whispers, "I have been praying that I might leave this world full of light. Please allow me to give my share of the food and water as a gift to my friends and ultimately to my newly found Savior."

I hesitate.

"Please allow me to do this thing," he pleads.

Laying my hand on his shoulder, I respond, "This is a noble thing that you are doing, and it does not go unnoticed in heaven or on earth, my friend."

"Peter, thank you for introducing me to the only One who has ever completely satisfied my searching heart. You have introduced me to the One who has unconditionally loved me. I am eternally grateful for you," Josiah states.

"And I am ever so grateful to the Lord for giving me the grace to be His witness. You are worth it, Josiah."

I am moved by Josiah's willingness to go hungry that others

might be full. I leave him and press on to Laban who refused to eat or drink very much for fear that there would not be enough for Eleazar and myself. I come to Eleazar who drinks long and deep. He eagerly eats the thick lentil paste from my filthy fingers.

After three servings, he says, "Peter, you have not eaten neither have you drank; the rest is for you."

I take a long drink; the water is warm, but it is wonderful! I do not drink it all, but save some for the others. Scooping up a handful of the lentil paste, I thank God for His provision. At which point Eleazar states matter of factly, "The wicked should not go unpunished."

"What makes you think that they will not be punished?"

"I have yet to see your God rise up in your defense. I see no justice being served here," Eleazar answers.

"There is a day coming when all who reject the Master will be judged and punished. Justice will fall on the wicked like a hammer falls on a nail when the Lion of Judah roars from His holy mountain. That is why I earnestly pray for those who do not yet know Him. That is why I boldly preach the good news. That is why I long for you to accept Jesus as your Savior, for that day will be terrible for those who reject the King of kings. God's desire is for none to perish, but for all to come to repentance," I answer.

"Why waste your time praying for men like me when you could be praying for yourself that you might not face persecution?" Eleazar asks with what sounds like a small measure of compassion.

"Oh, do not pray that I might not suffer persecution! Persecution has been my friend. It has caused me to grow in ways that I never would have. It has made me strong in that I have learned to lean on the Master. It has caused me to trust Him more than I would have had I lived a life of comfort and ease.

"I trust God to send me exactly what I need, both persecution and favor. I need both if I am to be all that I was created to be," I respond.

"This Jesus that you speak of is very different from the God that has been presented to me," Eleazar answers.

"You can know Him as I know Him, my brother. He is no respecter of persons," I say as I offer him another drink.

He refuses it saying, "Perhaps, some of the others would like more to drink. I have had enough."

At this point, they respond that their desire is for Eleazar to finish what remains. Holding the bucket to his mouth, I encourage him to drink. "Why would you be so generous to me, a Jew who does not believe in this Messiah, this Jesus? I must confess that I am not even sure if I believe in the God of our father Abraham anymore."

"It is an honor and privilege to give what little we have to you," Josiah says.

"Drink and eat, my brother," I say holding the bucket to his mouth.

"I may not believe your tales, but I am not heartless. I will not consume this by myself. You shall eat and drink with me, Peter," Eleazar responds taking another drink.

We share the water and the lentils. Then I make the long journey back to the door and place the bowl and bucket where the guard put them.

*The guards will think that the rodents ate the food and drank the water.*

Dragging my useless leg behind me, I crawl back to my friends, which completely exhausts my physical body.

*How much longer, Lord? My strength is gone, and my body cannot endure much more abuse. Oh, God grant that Eleazar and all that are in this place would come to know who You are! Give me Your words, give me Your heart, give me grace, I pray.*

Suddenly, Eleazar interrupts saying, "Perhaps, it would be wise for me to hear more about this Jesus. Not that I am thinking of making any changes in my life, but a wise man hears all the evidence before he makes a decision, and I have always prided myself in being wise. So Peter, if you are able, I am willing to listen."

"Nothing would make me happier, my friend! I do have a small problem though. I cannot remember what I last told you."

Surprisingly, Eleazar answers, "You told us of the Master forgiving that harlot, which exposed Simon's self-righteousness."

"Then let us begin there," I respond secretly smiling. *Eleazer has been listening! His heart is open!*

# CHAPTER TWENTY-EIGHT

We left Simon's house and followed Jesus through the various towns and villages in Galilee. Everywhere we went, the Master taught about the Kingdom of God, which was still a mystery to me.

Many followed the Master, but there were some who devoted themselves to care for Jesus and His twelve apostles. Among them was Mary of Magdala who Jesus delivered from seven demons. There was also Joanna, the wife of Chuza (Herod Antipas' business manager) and Suzanna. These faithful women and many others shared what they had with us using their own money to buy food for us and, with great joy, prepared our meals.[77] My beautiful wife joined us as often as she could, for she loved to sit at Jesus' feet and learn of His ways. Her heart was so hungry to know Him.

As we drew near Capernaum, many gathered around the Master. Standing just on the outskirts of the crowd was a group of Pharisees who watched Jesus like a cat watches a mouse.

Two men, escorting a third man between them, approached the Master. The eldest of them said, "Master, this man is blind."

The other added, "Not only is he blind, but neither can he speak."

Jesus looked on the man as a father looks on his hurting child.

Immediately, the Master stretched out His hand and touched the man. Suddenly, the man's downcast countenance changed. He lifted his head; his eyes were clear and bright. Throwing his arms in the air, he exclaimed, "I can see! I can see!"

His two friends embraced the man and shouted in unison, "And you can speak!"

The three friends locked arms as they danced in a circle laughing and crying. From out of the crowd, a voice shouted, "Who is this man that heals the blind and the dumb?"

"This man is not the son of David, is He?" another asked.

"Surely, He is not! He is from Galilee!" someone responded.

"Everyone knows that nothing good can come out of *Galilee!*" shouted a man standing nearby.

"But He does miracles!" another exclaimed.

The Pharisees turned their attention to the Master. Jesus, knowing the thoughts of men, looked at the Pharisees and said, "It would be very strange and highly improbable that Satan should cast himself out. If he did, then Satan's kingdom would be divided against itself. How could his kingdom stand if it were divided?"

He paused giving them time to respond. They merely straightened their shoulders and lifted their noses higher. The Master continued, "If I cast out demons by the power of Beelzebul, then by whose power do those in your company cast them out?"

Again, no answer. "This is why your own people prove you are wrong! However, if it is true that I drive out demons by the Spirit of God, then the Kingdom of the Messiah is about to be established among you," He stated.

With a thumbing of their noses, the Pharisees stormed off.

Undaunted, Jesus followed after them like a shepherd goes after a fox that threatens his sheep. He shouted, "How can anyone enter a strong man's house and carry off his possessions unless he first ties up the strong man? Once he has done that then he may do what he pleases with his goods.

"If a person is not with Me, he is against Me. The person who does not gather with Me scatters. A person is either on one side or the other.

It is not enough to keep from doing harm; one must also do good."

At this point, the Pharisees stopped, slowly turning; it was obvious that they were very angry. The Master did not let that stop Him. He continued, "When the unclean spirit goes out of a man, it passes through waterless places seeking rest, and not finding any, it says, 'I will return to my house from which I came.'

"And when it comes, it finds the house swept and put in order. So it goes and finds seven other spirits more evil than itself, and they go in and live there; and the last state of that man becomes worse than the first.

"People may be forgiven of any sin or any evil thing said against God, but they cannot be forgiven of blasphemy! If someone says something evil against Me, he can be forgiven. However, if someone blasphemes the Holy Spirit, he cannot be forgiven—not in this age or the age to come."

The Master's words gripped my heart like a man grips the railing of a sinking boat.

He continued, "Make a tree good, and its fruit will be good. Make a tree bad, and its fruit will be bad. Unless the heart is transformed, the life will never be reformed. A tree is known by its fruit.

"You are a brood of poisonous snakes. You are evil. Therefore, how can you say good things? Do you not know that a person speaks those things that flow out of his heart?

"A good man brings good things out of the good treasure of his heart, but an evil man brings out evil things from an evil treasure. Evil words are the natural, genuine product of an evil heart, just as good words are the natural, genuine product of a pure heart.

"I tell you, sometimes people talk without thinking. On the Judgment Day you will be held responsible for every word you have uttered. By your words, you will be justified, and by your words, you will be condemned.[78]

"Therefore, whatever is true, whatever is honorable, whatever is right, whatever is pure, whatever is lovely, whatever is of good reputation, if there is any excellence and if anything worthy of praise, let your mind dwell on these things. The things that you have learned and received and heard and seen in Me, practice these things; and the God of peace will be with you."[79]

The Pharisees glared at Him, their faces red with rage. A woman in the crowd suddenly cried out, "Blessed is the mother who gave birth to You and the breasts at which You nursed!"

Jesus, with His eyes fixed on the Pharisees responded, "On the contrary, blessed are those who hear the word of God and do it."[80]

# CHAPTER TWENTY-NINE

Eleazar interrupts, "I have never heard of a rabbi challenging the Pharisees in such a blatant, insulting way and getting away with it! The Pharisees are beyond reproach, yet you claim that Jesus publicly condemned them and lived to tell about it. There is no way that He could have called them a brood of poisonous snakes and accused them of being evil without suffering the consequences. What you claim is not possible—not in Israel, not among our Jewish leaders!"

Trying to move my very swollen leg to a less painful position I answer, "I did not claim that Jesus suffered no consequences from His actions. He certainly did, but Jesus feared no man, Eleazar. He did not compromise in word or in deed, neither did He fail to speak the truth. But, I must admit that I was just as shocked as you when I heard Jesus speak so boldly. At the time, I thought it quite foolish of Him. But, I later came to realize that Jesus loved these men so deeply that He had to speak the truth. His desire was and still is for all to know Him, which includes those who are His enemies.

"Jesus was fierce in His love and fierce in bringing truth. He was and is a good Shepherd who always goes after anything that threatens to harm His sheep. And that was exactly what Jesus did, consistently and with lovingkindness. He understood the harm that the Pharisees' teachings were doing to the people of Israel, so He had to speak the truth.

"Jesus was the boldest person I had ever met, but that was not what impacted me the most about Him. What impacted me the most was His great love for everyone, including the Scribes and Pharisees. Time and time again, I witnessed His deep desire for the Pharisees to be saved from their fruitless way of life and be transformed into His image.

"Lest you think that all of the Scribes and Pharisees rejected Jesus, I must tell you that there were some who embraced Him as the Son of God, but sadly, there were many who did not. In defense of the Lord, not that He needs anyone to defend Him, but it was obvious that Jesus desperately loved the Scribes and Pharisees, and that is the reason He spoke the truth to them."

Eleazar responds, "From my experiences with the Pharisees, Jesus was either extremely brave or absolutely foolish to so boldly confront such respected and powerful men as these. Surely He knew they could have Him killed?"

"Jesus most certainly knew that, but His face was set like flint on His Father's will, and His purpose was firmly established. No power on earth or in heaven could keep Him from seeing its fulfillment. He knew exactly what He was doing. He also knew that He would eventually die at the hands of those men," I respond.

"Indeed?," Eleazar replies his voice fading into the darkness.

In quietness, I wait and pray.

"I am ready to hear more," Eleazar finally states.

I respond, "Eleazar, you remind me of another Jewish brother, a man named Paul. In the beginning, Paul, who was then called Saul, hated this message to the point that he arrested and persecuted men and women for being Christians. But, one eventful day, as he was on his way to wreak havoc among the Christians in Damascus, Jesus appeared to him on the road. From that day forward, Paul became a believer, and to this day continues, if he is still alive, to preach the good news that Jesus Christ came to seek and save the lost. I pray that you, too, might—."

Angry voices in the hall and the piercing snap of a whip cause me to stop and pray, "Father, I ask You to intervene. Send help, I pray. Send angels. Send the Comforter, and help this poor soul."

A not so distant door opens followed by more shouting and more cracking of a whip. I continue to intercede. Justus, Josiah and Laban are praying as well.

Sweat forms on my forehead, and runs down my face stinging my eyes. I have a raging fever. I feel very sick and very exhausted. The room spins out of control. I lean my head against the stone wall in an effort to steady myself. I do not know when, but at some point, I fall asleep.

"Peter, wake up," a voice whispers. A hand on my shoulder gently shakes me. "Peter, you must wake up. I have brought news concerning your wife, Miriam."

That piece of information is all I need to draw me out of my delirious state. I open my eyes and, in the dim light, see Malchus' smiling face looking down at me. "You have news of my wife?" I ask, my voice cracking.

Feeling both excitement and dread, I wipe my sweaty face on my tattered sleeve. My heart is racing like a runaway horse. Images of my wife's beautiful face flash before me. I can see her delightful smile and charming dark brown eyes.

"Peter, your wife is alive," Malchus states.

Taking a deep breath, I quietly ask, "How is she, Malchus? Is she well?"

Malchus answers, "Peter, she is as well as she can be in a place like this. Cyrus, the guard in charge of her has done a good job of protecting her and also providing food and water for her. He told me that your wife has led many of the guards to Jesus as well as most of the other prisoners on her floor. Cyrus himself has become a believer because of the testimony of your wife."

"Oh, how I praise the Lord! Oh, how my heart rejoices! There is absolutely nothing as beautiful or as wonderful as knowing that the one you love is in love with the Lord and faithfully serves Him! Thank you, my friend! You have brought great joy and much peace to this old man's heart!"[81]

Tears of joy pour down my wrinkled face.

"I am happy to serve you, my friend and brother."

"Tell me, have you seen her?" I ask.

"I have, and what a delight she is! Cyrus allowed me to spend a short time with her. The first thing she did was ask me if I knew Jesus. Her second question was about you. She then gave me this—."

Malchus reaches into his pocket and places a locket of grey hair in my hand saying, "She ripped this from her head and asked me to give it to you. She said, 'Would you tell Peter that I love him dearly and miss him immensely? Tell him that I constantly pray for him.'

"I promised her I would. Then, she prayed for me, and what a beautiful prayer it was! I reluctantly left assuring her that I would give you her message."

"Your words are music to my ears, my friend," I respond overwhelmed with emotions.

"Peter, your wife is full of the Holy Spirit and strong in the Lord. Cyrus told me that he often sneaks her out of the cell to pray for those who are sick and dying, and most often they are healed. He intentionally places those who have never heard the good news in her cell, and they almost all become believers!"

"She is the love of my life on this earth just as the Lord is the love of my life spiritually. This is wonderful news that you have brought to me today, my friend. Oh, how I rejoice in the Lord! If my leg was not broken, I would be dancing and shouting and jumping right now!"

"I hate the fact that you are a prisoner and I am a free man," Malchus says as he inspects my wounds.

"But, Malchus, I am a free man! Just as Miriam is free and Laban and Justus and Josiah and soon to be Eleazar! For whom Christ sets free is free indeed! I am free where it counts, my friend!"

"I know that this is true, but I hate to see you suffer so much."

"My suffering is temporary. But, speaking of freedom. Josiah told me how you rescued me from the mouth of the lions. Thank you, my brother, thank you for laying your life down for me."

"I wasn't the one who rescued you from those lions, my friend. It was the Lord who shut their mouths just as He did for Daniel! I have never seen anything like that—those lions would not come anywhere near you! It was truly amazing to see!"

"How is it that you have not been arrested?" I ask.

"I do not know the answer to that question. I certainly expected to be, but it never happened. It is as if no one saw me drag you inside. No one has said a word to me about it, not even the Centurion who has charge over me. I have not been treated any differently, neither does it appear that I am being watched. I can not explain it, my brother. It is a mystery indeed."

"According to His plan, the Lord has protected you, my friend. He has hidden you in His great love!"

"Peter, I am ready to die for Him, if that should be His plan for my life. I fully understand that this life is not the end, that it is a springboard for every soul who enters into a relationship with the King. A King who longs for a close, personal relationship with His sons and daughters. My life is mostly about preparing for what is to come."

"Malchus, what you say is the truth, but so many people live as though this life is all there is."

"I thank God for revealing the truth to His children!" he replies.

"Malchus, I don't mean to change the subject, but would you tell me more about my wife? How did she look? Is her health good? Is she suffering or in pain?"

"She is thin and has definitely been through a lot, but her eyes are full of light. Her spirit is strong, and her heart is filled with great peace. In spite of prison life and all of its challenges, she appears to be doing okay. I would tell you if I found her otherwise."

"Malchus, if you see her again would you please tell her that I am in constant prayer for her and tell her that I love her? Would you also tell her that I look forward to the moment when she and I will step out of these mortal bodies and into the glorious light of the Lord's presence?"

"Perhaps, you would like to tell her yourself?" Malchus asks as a broad smile covers his youthful face.

"Malchus, what are you saying?"

"I am simply asking if you would like to see your wife? You see, Peter, Cyrus is moving her to this floor tomorrow. He has agreed, if I can keep the other guards away, to bring her to see you for a brief moment."

"Please tell me that you told him you would do so?"

"I told him that I would do whatever I had to do to clear a path for him. So, my friend, it seems that you have a big day ahead of you!" Malchus joyfully exclaims as he gently pats my shoulder.

I cannot respond because the lump in my throat is so large that I can barely swallow.

Malchus asks, "Peter, what are your injuries?"

"My leg is broken as are several ribs. I must have an infection somewhere since I am burning up with fever, but it could be worse; I could have been supper for several very hungry lions."

"For which fact I am ever so thankful. I shall pray for you, and then I must go," he says as he lays his hand on me and prays for my complete healing.

He tears strips of cloth from his outer garment and, as carefully as he can, wraps my leg in an effort to immobilize it. Promising to remember me in his prayers, he bids us farewell. Before the door closes behind him, I am already lost in thoughts of tomorrow.

Holding tightly the locket of hair, I say, "Eleazar, Justus, Josiah, Laban, I can scarcely believe it! After all these months, I will get to see my wife! What an answer to my prayers! What a gift from the Lord! He has answered exceedingly, abundantly beyond all that I could ask or think!"

Filled with overwhelming joy, I cry out with a loud voice, "Salvation belongs to our God who sits on the throne and to the Lamb! Blessing and glory and wisdom and thanksgiving and honor and power and might be to our God forever and ever!"[82]

My heart is so full of love and adoration that I do not stop even when my cell door swings opens and an enraged Brutus storms in. I barely feel his whip and scarcely hear his vile words. The only thing that I am really aware of is the fact that I am loved by the Lord. I belong to another world, to another Master whose extravagant, infinite love for me causes my heart to sing!

Frustrated, Brutus stops and walks toward the door, but suddenly stops. Slowly turning around, he says, "Deny Jesus, or I will beat one of your fellow prisoners!"

"As much as I love my friends, I cannot deny that Jesus is the Son of God."

My heart is filled with anguish.

"Then deny this," he says as his whip cuts through the air and lands across Eleazar' shoulders.

As Brutus repeatedly lashes out at Eleazar, I pray for them both.

"So, Peter, is that enough to change your mind or shall I choose another of your friends?" Brutus asks.

"Peter, do not worry about us," Justus encourages me.

"What do we have here?" Brutus asks, "Another Christian perhaps?"

"I am indeed a Christian. I would be foolish to not be," Justus responds.

I pray harder.

Brutus stands over Justus like Goliath stood over David.

*It is obvious that Brutus is furious. Help, Lord!*

Suddenly, a guard appears at the door saying, "Brutus, the Centurion has sent for you. He said that it was important."

Kicking Justus in the side, he says, "I guess it's your lucky day."

As soon as the door shuts I ask, "Eleazar, are you okay?"

Eleazar merely groans deeply.

"And what of you, Justus?" I ask.

He responds, "Peter, I did it! I remained true! I have been secretly afraid that I would deny Jesus should I ever be faced with persecution. But, I didn't! I was ready to die for Him, Peter!"

"There is no greater love than for a man to lay down his life for a friend, and that is exactly what you did," I respond.

"Eleazar," Justus says, "I will pray for you."

"As will I," I say.

Laban and Josiah assure him of their prayers, too.

I crawl to Eleazar and pray for him until he falls asleep. It is not long before I join him and dream that Jesus steps out of the darkness with my precious wife clinging to His arm. They walk towards me, both are smiling, both are beautiful and both are happy to see me. Tears of joy and longing sweep over me like the wind sweeps over the sea. I try to stand but cannot.

My Beloved looks directly at me; His eyes, as always, are filled with great tenderness and complete understanding. As He joins me on the rough stone floor, He speaks, and His voice is like the sound of a thunderous waterfall, which causes my insides to quake. He says, "Peter, you are dearly loved. I know that you have endured much for My sake; it has all been duly recorded, My friend. You are beautiful in the sight of heaven and in My eyes."

"Oh, Lord, it is You who is altogether beautiful! Your beauty surpasses everything this world has to offer and Your love is better than wine. Indeed, my Lord, You are the one who is beautiful!"[83]

"And I have clothed you in My garments of righteousness. I have fashioned and formed you into My image. Look and see, My friend."

I look down expecting to see filthy rags, but find that I am shining like the Son and dressed in robes of fine linen. "You have indeed given me a gift that I could never earn neither could I ever deserve."

"Such is the gift of eternal life, My friend," He responds.

Laying my head on His chest I say, "I long for the day when nothing separates us. Tell me, dear Lord, how much longer must I wait? How much longer before I am with You where You are?"

He remains silent. I look up into His glorious eyes. The Master smiles, and a light that is brighter than the noon day sun explodes from within His very being!

"I shall never see again!" I cry out in glorious agony.

The Master laughs.

*Oh, how I have missed His laugh!*

He whispers, "I am always with you, Peter. I am always here."

Resting my head back on His chest, I say, "Oh, divine Master, You shine brighter than the sun! You are outstanding among ten thousand, fairer than the sons of men and Your love has transformed my willful, prideful, selfish heart!"

"And your voluntary love and sacrificial devotion has conquered the heart of this King—a King who cannot be conquered," He responds.

"How is that possible?"

"You were created for love, my friend. You were created to be loved and to love"

"Master, there is no one I would rather be with. Therefore, I will contend until the end. I will press on in order that I may lay hold of Your free gift. I press on toward the goal. I will not give up or give in! I will love You unto the end, my Lord!"[84]

Jesus responds, "Put Me like a seal over your heart, over all that you do for Me, for love is as strong as death. Many waters cannot quench love, nor will rivers overflow it. Persecution cannot. Rejection is powerless against such love. Fear is cast out by it. Death is swallowed up in it. Pain and suffering are healed by it. Pursue Love, My friend, for love never fails."[85]

"I shall, Lord!"

"Peter, I shall grant you the desires of your heart. You shall soon be with Me where I am, but first there is someone you long to see."

He then turns to Miriam and motions for her to join us. As she draws near, I gaze into the beautiful eyes of my Savior and whisper, "Your ways are perfect!"

Jesus stands and places my wife's hand in mine and then takes a step back.

Miriam joins me on the floor. I stare at her for the longest time. Finally, I say, "I have missed you terribly and have prayed for you faithfully."

She leans over and kisses me saying, "My husband, you have loved me well."

"And you have loved me so much more than I ever deserved," I respond.

"Peter, this has been a good season, for I have learned that strength is not what qualifies me; weakness does. I have learned to love even my enemies. And I have learned to cling to the Rock when the ground shakes beneath my feet."

My beloved wife then turns to Jesus and says, "Do you see the stripes on his back? Do you see his broken leg? And what of his fever?

Will You heal him, my beloved King and Master?"

Jesus responds, "I see all things, Miriam. I share in his pain."

Laying His nail-scarred hand on my shoulder, He says, "By My stripes, you are healed."

With those words, I am suddenly wide awake.

*What was that? Was I dreaming?*

I move my leg and quickly discover that it is still very much broken. My wounds are just as painful as before. Miriam is not here, and neither is the Master.

*It was nothing but a dream!*

My heart sinks. I can feel the demon of despair hovering over me eager to get its slimy, poisonous claws in my mind, so I do the very thing that creature hates—I lift my voice in worship:

"Oh, my God and King,
through the storm I sing!
Hide me under Your mighty wings.
You are my dream come true
and I have eyes for only You!
The one thing I desire is to be with You,
    for then I will be brand new!

"Risen Lord and coming King!
You sit on a throne holding a scepter of justice!
While I was still a sinner, You died for me!
And Your eye is on the sparrow;
Your eye is on me!
It is well with my soul because
the King of kings loves me!
Oh beautiful, wonderful Savior,
how can I love You more?
Help me find a way, Jesus!"

Eleazar jabs me with his elbow, grunting. I stop long enough to ask, "Eleazar, how can I help you?"

"You can shut up!" he answers.

"If I do not sing I will be swallowed up in despair, my brother."

I quietly pray, "Father, I ask You to comfort Eleazar and heal his wounds and his heart. I ask You to make a way for me to see Miriam, but should it not happen I will still love You! I will still worship You because You satisfy my heart in a way that nothing else can. I will never stop proclaiming that You are gracious, slow to anger, abounding in lovingkindness, and You are good to all!"

I can feel the demon of despair retreating. I am filled with peace and joy. I lift my voice again and sing:

"I will sing of your unfailing love,
for You have been good to me.
You will always be good to me!
I trust in Your unfailing love![86]
The God who created heaven and earth
is my only hope.
You are my only prayer,
so I will wait for You to come!
Oh, how glorious! Oh how wonderful You are!"

Eleazar curses loudly.

"Oh, how good God is!" I shout.

The sound of shuffling feet outside my door only drives me deeper into the heart of God. The key turns in the lock and I whisper into the darkness, "Come what may, I rest in your faithfulness!"[77]

*To be continued....*

And after you have suffered for a little while,
the God of all grace,
who called you to His eternal glory in Christ,
will Himself perfect, confirm,
strengthen and establish you.

To Him be dominion forever and ever, Amen.

—Simon Peter

(I Peter 5:10-11)

## A note from the Artist...

My emotions have been on the surface while creating this companion painting to Rhonda Calhoun's book, "Simon Peter and the Master."

In preparation for painting this scene, I contemplated on Peter and what he would be thinking as he sat chained in a dark, dank prison cell awaiting his execution. Tears came from deep in my heart as I imagined Peter immersed in reflection, remembering that first encounter with his Lord who said, "Come and I will make you a fisher of men." Peter did follow and he walked into the impossible. His contemplation brings a depth of the truth that Christ is always asking us to get out of the boat and walk on water—even until the end of our lives. The smile on the Master's lips is an indication that He endured the cross for the joy set before Him. Peter sees the blood flowing from His hands and feet—that which was to come for the sins of all mankind (Heb. 12:2).

Peter's life is fading away—the old will be made new. The promise of the resurrection is vivid in the figure of Christ as He bids Peter to "Come once again, My old and faithful friend, and walk with Me upon the water." This is our destiny as believers in the ONE who said, "I am the way, the truth and the life. No one comes to the

Father except through Me." (John 14:6).

Peter himself preached under the inspiration of the Holy Spirit, "There is no other name (Jesus Christ) under heaven given among men by which we must be saved." (Acts 4:12).

Won't you get out of your boat and follow Him? I promise you, it will be worth it!

Pam Macchi

# ENDNOTES

## CHAPTER ONE
[1] Psalm 25:6-7
[2] Psalm 142:5-7
[3] I John 4:18
[4] I Peter 4:16,19

## CHAPTER TWO
[5] Matthew 4:18-22; Luke 5:1-11
[6] Matthew 3:1-4
[7] Mark 1:7-8
[8] John 1:29,31
[9] Matthew 3:13-15
[10] Luke 3:21-22
[11] John 1:29-42

## CHAPTER THREE
[12] Luke 9:1
[13] Matthew 16:13-19

## CHAPTER FOUR
[14] John 1:43-51
[15] John 2:1-10
[16] John 2:11-13
[17] John 2:14-17
[18] John 3:1-21

[19] John 3:22-36
[20] John 4:1-54

## CHAPTER FIVE
[21] John 21:25

## CHAPTER SIX
[22] Matthew 4:12; Mark 1:14; Luke 4:14, Mark 1:15
[23] Luke 5:1-11

## CHAPTER SEVEN

## CHAPTER EIGHT
[24] Mark 1:21-28; Luke 4:31-37
[25] the actual 'remedy' of the Pharisees in that day
[26] Matthew 8:14-17; Mark 1:29-34; Luke 4:38-41
[27] Luke 4:42-44; Mark 1:35-39
[28] Matthew 4:23-25
[29] Matthew 4:13-17
[30] the actual Sabbath prayer and order of service
[31] Luke 4:15-32;42-44

## CHAPTER NINE
[32] James 1:17

## CHAPTER TEN
[33] Matthew 8:1-4; Mark 1:40-45; Luke 5:12-16; Leviticus 13:49
[34] Matthew 5:17
[35] Psalm 106:1
[36] Psalm 89:6-9
[37] John 5:39
[38] Matthew 9:1-8; Mark 2:1-12; Luke 5:17-26

## CHAPTER ELEVEN
[39] Joel 2:13

## CHAPTER TWELVE
[40] Matthew 9:9-13; Mark 2:13-17; Luke 5:27-32
[41] Hosea 6:6
[42] Revelation 19:7-13

[43] Matthew 9:14-17; Mark 2:18-22; Luke 5:33-39
[44] Isaiah 53:7
[45] Exodus 20:10
[46] John 5:1-47

## CHAPTER THIRTEEN

## CHAPTER FOURTEEN
[47] Deuteronomy 5:14
[48] Matthew 12:1-8; Mark 2:23-28; Luke 6:1-5
[49] Matthew 12:9-14; Mark 3:1-6; Luke 6:6-11
[50] Matthew12:15-21; Mark 3:7-17; Luke 6:17-19

## CHAPTER FIFTEEN

## CHAPTER SIXTEEN
[51] Isaiah 9:1-2
[52] I Corinthians 13:4-8, 13
[53] Joel 2:13
[54] Matthew 10:2-4; Mark 3:13-19; Luke 6:12-16
[55] Matthew 5:1-6:23

## CHAPTER SEVENTEEN

## CHAPTER EIGHTEEN
[56] Matthew 7:1-29; Luke 6:20-49

## CHAPTER NINETEEN
[57] Song of Solomon 6:4,10; Song of Solomon 8:5

## CHAPTER TWENTY
[58] Matthew 8:5-13; Luke 7:1-10; Isaiah 49:12-13

## CHAPTER TWENTY-ONE
[59] John 20:29

## CHAPTER TWENTY-TWO
[60] Luke 7:11-17
[61] Psalm 46:1-2
[62] Job 19:25

## CHAPTER TWENTY-THREE
[63] Matthew 11:2-15; Luke 7:18-23

## CHAPTER TWENTY-FOUR
[64] Malachi 3:1
[65] Luke 7:24-35
[66] Matthew 11:7-30

## CHAPTER TWENTY-FIVE
[67] Psalm 116:15
[68] I Peter 1:8-9
[69] Romans 12:17, 19, 21

## CHAPTER TWENTY-SIX
[70] Luke 7:36-50

## CHAPTER TWENTY-SEVEN
[71] Song of Solomon 7:10
[72] Psalm 97:10
[73] Philippians 1:29
[74] Psalm 27:1-6
[75] Psalm 18:1-6
[76] I Peter 4:12-14

## CHAPTER TWENTY-EIGHT
[77] Luke 8:1-3
[78] Matthew 12:22-37; Mark 3:20-3-; Luke 11:14-23
[79] Philippians 4:8-9
[80] Luke 11:27-28

## CHAPTER TWENTY-NINE
[81] III John 3
[82] Revelation 7:10,12
[83] Song of Solomon 1:2
[84] Philippians 3:12-14
[85] Song of Solomon 8:6-7
[86] Jeremiah 33:11

## OTHER BOOKS BY THE AUTHOR

**THE BRIDE** by Rhonda Calhoun is a fascinating and life-changing allegory based on the Song of Solomon. *The Bride'* takes you on a journey with a young shepherdess as the King of kings wins her heart and reveals His glorious character. The truths brought out by this book may forever change the way you see yourself and your King.

**BLESSED ARE THE POOR** by Rhonda Calhoun is a gripping collection of real-life stories from Danny and Rhonda's ministry with the poor and homeless of Kansas City. Each chapter is a portrait of a man, woman, or child who lives in drastic poverty and whose lives have impacted the author in profound ways. This book not only paints a picture of what it is like to live in poverty, sickness and hopelessness, but it also describes the miraculous ways God meets the needs of His children. Even though their circumstances may seem impossible, in the midst of darkness, hope rises and love flows. Your heart will certainly be impacted and enlarged as you read these powerful testimonies of extravagant faith.

**FATHER HEART OF GOD STUDY MANUAL** is an excellent 100+ page study manual. Rhonda digs deep into the word of God revealing the Father's heart for those living in poverty. You will also discover how extravagant our Father is to all of His children regardless of their social status. After all, we all look the same at the foot of the cross.

**THE BRIDE STUDY MANUAL** can be used alone or with *The Bride'*. This in-depth study manual goes through the Song of Solomon verse by verse and phrase by phrase explaining, in easy to understand language, this highly symbolic book. The manual also includes a fascinating teaching on the Jewish betrothal customs during the time of Jesus. This manual is perfect for those who desire to dig deep into the bridal message. It is a great bible study tool for both individuals and groups.

**KID'S EXPLOSION MANUAL** explains how to organize a fun, bible-based outreach to children in your neighborhood, church, park, or inner city. Part One tells David's story and his first visit to one of our Kid's Explosion's, which gives you an insider's view of what the program looks like. Part Two is step-by-step instructions of how to start, organize and run your own outreach. The manual includes many helpful tools such as lists of games, memory verses, and bible stories.

## TEACHING DVD'S AND CD'S:

**SONG OF SOLOMON** Join instructor Rhonda Calhoun as she teaches in the Forerunner School of Ministry at the International house of Prayer in Kansas City. Your life will be enriched and your heart ignited as you journey with her through this incredible story describing the infinite love the King has for us, His bride. Rhonda's insightful and delightful teaching thoroughly and explores the glorious truths found in each verse of this eight chapter Song. She lays a strong foundation for the bridal paradigm using numerous scriptures and also the Jewish betrothal customs during Jesus' day, which clearly portrays our relationship with the Bridegroom King. Available in a 10-DVD set or 19-CD set.

**THE REAL CINDERELLA STORY** is a message shared by Rhonda Calhoun. This fascinating teaching reveals the Bride of Christ and her Bridegroom as told through the Cinderella fairy tale. This heart-warming, eye-opening teaching will inspire and create a greater love in your heart for your Bridegroom King. Great for children from 10 to 90, male or female. (CD)

**JOURNEY INTO THE PROPHETIC** is an excellent two part teaching by Rhonda Calhoun on the wonders, difficulties and delights of following the Master. (2-CD set)

**JEWISH BETROTHAL CUSTOMS** This eye-opening teaching by Rhonda Calhoun explores the engagement customs during the time of Jesus and how they relate to us today. It paints a clear picture of the  relationship He desires with His disciples. You will be amazed at the truths you find hidden in the Lord's Supper.

## WORSHIP CD'S:

**ONE THING I DESIRE** is an outstanding intercessory worship CD from the International House of Prayer in Kansas City. The worship songs and intercessory prayers are taken straight from the Song of Solomon and Psalms. The singers sing the scriptures in the form of prayer while others sing the Lord's response to their cries. This highly anointed worship CD will quickly become one of your  favorites.

**THE FATHER'S LOVE LETTER** is a most powerful and heart touching CD by Father Heart Communications. The first 'song' is actually a love letter from your Father using the scriptures. The voice of a kind and loving father reads the love letter to you while anointed music plays in the background. The second is a reading of the scriptures that speak of how your Father feels about you. Beautiful music plays in the background. The third is a beautiful response to the Father, which will bring you to tears. (Words by Barry Adams © 1999. Music: Robert Critchley © 2000 Wild Ox Publishing. Naration: Roy Lamont.)

**BETTER THAN LIFE** by Julie Meyer is an excellent worship CD that was recorded at the International House of Prayer in Kansas City.  Julie is an anointed and very gifted worship leader. This new CD brings the listener into the realization that we are lovely to God even in our weakest moments.  Her worship songs will encourage your heart and lead you into the presence of God.

## AUDIO TAPES:

**LOVE THAT CONQUERS WEAKNESS** is an inspiring message by Rhonda Calhoun. This message takes you on a journey revealing the truth that love is stronger than death and stronger than the grave. Rhonda challenges the hearer to receive the unconditional love of Christ as the free gift that it is, regardless of your past sins or accomplishments.

## OTHER RESOURCES:

**SONG OF SOLOMON** anointing oil. This sweet smelling oil is made from the 8 spices listed in Sg. of Sol. 4:13-14. This delightfully fragrant oil comes in a small bottle, which is easy to carry in pocket or purse.

**WITNESS BRACELET** is a bracelet of different colored beads, which represent the journey of life from birth to death with salvation occurring along the way. Included with the bracelet is a detailed explanation of what each color represents and how to use the bracelet to witness to others. This bracelet is for old or young, male or female.

# PRODUCT ORDER FORM:

| BOOKS: | QTY. | PRICE | TOTAL |
|---|---|---|---|
| SIMON PETER AND THE MASTER | ____ | $ 15.00 | ____ |
| BLESSED ARE THE POOR | ____ | $ 10.00 | ____ |
| THE FATHER HEART OF GOD STUDY MANUAL | ____ | $ 20.00 | ____ |
| THE BRIDE | ____ | $ 16.00 | ____ |
| THE BRIDE STUDY MANUAL | ____ | $ 20.00 | ____ |
| THE KID'S EXPLOSION MANUAL | ____ | $ 20.00 | ____ |

## TEACHING DVD'S & CD'S:

| | QTY. | PRICE | TOTAL |
|---|---|---|---|
| THE SONG OF SOLOMON CLASS | | | |
| (10 DVD SET) | ____ | $110.00 | ____ |
| (19 CD SET) | ____ | $110.00 | ____ |
| JOURNEY INTO THE PROPHETIC (2 CD SET) | ____ | $ 15.00 | ____ |
| JEWISH BETROTHAL CUSTOMS | ____ | $ 7.00 | ____ |
| THE REAL CINDERELLA STORY | ____ | $ 7.00 | ____ |

## WORSHIP DVD'S

| | QTY. | PRICE | TOTAL |
|---|---|---|---|
| ONE THING I DESIRE | ____ | $ 15.00 | ____ |
| THE FATHER'S LOVE LETTER | ____ | $ 13.00 | ____ |
| BETTER THAN LIFE | ____ | $ 15.00 | ____ |

## AUDIO TAPE:

| | QTY. | PRICE | TOTAL |
|---|---|---|---|
| LOVE THAT CONQUERS WEAKNESS | ____ | $ 5.00 | ____ |

## ANOINTING OIL:

| | QTY. | PRICE | TOTAL |
|---|---|---|---|
| SONG OF SOLOMON ANOINTING OIL | ____ | $ 7.00 | ____ |

## WITNESS BRACELET

| | QTY. | PRICE | TOTAL |
|---|---|---|---|
| WITNESS BRACELET | ____ | $ 3.00 | ____ |

SUBTOTAL $_____

Shipping, add 10% (minimum of $2.00) $_____

(U.S. funds only) **Total Enclosed** $_____

SEND PAYMENT WITH ORDER FORM TO:

**Heart Publishing**
**12905 South 71 Hwy. #177**
**Grandview, MO  64030**

Mailing address: (please print)

Name: _____

Street: _____

City_____State _____ Zip_____

**We  Accept  Master Card, Visa, or Discover:**

Card Number: _____

Expiration Date: _____

V -Number: _____
(last 3 numbers on back of card on signature line)

Phone Number: _____

**For phone orders, bookstore orders**
**or quantity discounts call:**

**816-522-9011**
**or**

**order from our on-line bookstore at:**
**www.harvesthome.org**